TECHNICAL
REPORTING

TECHNICAL REPORTING

REVISED EDITION

Joseph N. Ulman, Jr.

Consumer Reports Magazine

Jay R. Gould

Rensselaer Polytechnic Institute

HOLT, RINEHART AND WINSTON
New York · Chicago · San Francisco
Toronto · London

PREFACE
TO THE REVISED EDITION

Audience

This book is addressed primarily to students and practitioners of engineering and the sciences who have reached the point at which they have reporting jobs to do and have something to say. This stage is attained by most technical students in their sophomore, junior, or senior year; by a very few in their freshman year; and by some not until they are in graduate school or in industry. Only at this stage are most of them receptive to instruction in technical reporting, and only then do they have genuinely realistic subject matter to work with.

Content

The first edition of *Technical Reporting* was based on material used at the Massachusetts Institute of Technology for instruction that fell into two main categories: (1) a course in technical writing offered by the Department of Humanities and (2) instruction given in connection with reports required of the students by several of the professional departments (Mechanical, Civil, Electrical, and Marine Engineering, Physics, Geology, and others). The present revision and enlargement stems from experience at Rensselaer Polytechnic Institute, both in undergraduate courses and the Graduate Program in Technical Writing, and in the Technical Writers' Institute held each summer for professional technical writers and supervisors.

Entirely new material includes Chapter 4 on Technical Description, Chapter 9 on the Thesis, and Chapter 11 on Instructional Writing. Additional kinds of reports and variations of form are discussed in Chapters 6 and 7 on Informal and Formal Reports, and a number of illustrative specimens have been added to the Appendix. Chapter 10 on Technical Papers and Articles and Chapter 12 on Oral Reports and Speaking in

Public contain a considerable quantity of new material. In addition, further explanation and new examples have been added throughout the text wherever teaching experience has indicated the need for them.

Finally, suggestions for written exercises have been included at the ends of a number of chapters. We feel that the most realistic and fruitful writing assignments, with a maximum of motivation for the student, are likely to originate in the professional or technical departments, in connection with technical or experimental investigations being performed by the students. But for those institutions where instruction in technical writing is given by members of the English Department independently of their colleagues in the technical fields, these exercises should prove useful.

In *Technical Reporting* we have stressed the thesis that one of the commonest and most serious faults in technical and scientific writing is the burial of the important, fundamental ideas under a mass of detail— the masking of the forest by the trees. Many of the textbooks on technical writing seem to suffer from this very fault.

Accordingly, *Technical Reporting* stresses the principles—some of them quite elementary—that seem to be most overlooked by technical writers. This policy has permitted us to treat fully those subjects that are included.

For instance, we have not presented the section on old-fashioned business-letter clichés that appears in many textbooks in this field. Practically no writer under 75 ever indulges in the "Yours of the 20th inst. to hand . . ." pattern, and there seems no reason to burden a younger generation with warnings against it. On the other hand, we have devoted a lot of attention to some principles for making graphs and curves clear and easy to read—some principles that are commonly overlooked by practicing professional men as well as students.

Another valid reason for omitting a subject is the strong likelihood that most students will be unable or unwilling to remember it or use it. For example, the usual handbook on composition lists a dozen or more uses of the comma, most of them described in technical grammatical terms and given without reason or justification. The average man just doesn't remember all these formal rules; indeed he probably never understands many of them. Consequently he dismisses from his mind all he has been told about the comma, and punctuates improperly and confusingly. In the section on punctuation in this book we have suggested a few simple and easily remembered general rules of thumb for the use of the comma; but we have dwelt in detail on the three comma rules that we believe must be observed rigorously and consistently in order to eliminate ambiguity. Furthermore, we have explained *why* each rule is used, because most people neither remember unjustified rules nor employ them intelligently.

Acknowledgments

For their helpful criticism and advice we are indebted to Professor Lynwood S. Bryant of MIT and Mr. Kenneth A. Stonex, Assistant Director of the General Motors Proving Ground. Mr. Joseph J. Connelly, Mr. Norman L. Daggett, and Mr. Charles L. Miller, all at one time or another connected with MIT, have kindly permitted us to use their reports as specimens. Dr. Sterling P. Olmsted, head of the Department of Language and Literature at RPI, and Professor Douglas H. Washburn, also at RPI, have permitted us to use material previously compiled by them.

Thanks are also due to the Hercules Powder Company for permission to reproduce the report outline from *Hercules Technical Reports—A Guide to Their Preparation;* to Chrysler Corporation for permission to reproduce the report outline from their *Technical Report Manual;* to International Business Machines Corporation for permission to reproduce part of their manual *Digitally Controlled Tube Tester;* to Oak Ridge National Laboratory (operated by the Union Carbide and Carbon Corporation for the United States Atomic Energy Commission) for permission to reproduce portions of the report *Radio-Frequency Oscillators for Determination of Alkali;* to John F. Rider, Publisher, Inc., for permission to reproduce from the *Trouble Shooter's Manual* the diagrams of Figs. 12 and 13; and to Arthur D. Little, Inc., for permission to quote part of "The Turbo-Encabulator."

J. N. U., Jr.
J. R. G.

September 1958

CONTENTS

PART III.   TOOLS AND METHODS

PART I

BASIC ISSUES

1. A SELLING JOB

We may as well face the fact: the typical undergraduate regards the writing of reports as a dull and superfluous chore. Consequently, he has little desire for instruction in technical writing, and he approaches classes in this subject with a wary, bored resistance.

One of the main reasons for this state of affairs is that the undergraduate—particularly in his earlier years—seems to have very little to say. As he progresses through college and on into graduate school or industry, he develops a body of knowledge. At some time in his career he acquires some information or some ideas that he wants to pass on to others. Only then does he wish for instruction in technical reporting. But then, all too often, he has finished his schooling, and he has to get his instruction the hard way.

Thus this book, along with most others in its field, seems to be obliged to begin with a selling job.

1.1 The Importance of Technical Reporting

The complexity of an organization increases exponentially with its size. And as the complexity goes up, so too does the need for written records and communications. Only through a full exchange of information can the various divisions of a large organization coordinate their efforts effectively.

But even the small organization has a vital need for accurate technical reporting. How was a special part fabricated last year? How was a test performed? What are the precautions to be observed with a seldom-used instrument? Written records furnish authoritative answers to many questions such as these, and increase the efficiency of the organization that maintains a rigorous reporting procedure.

Some engineering and scientific organizations do nothing but investigation, testing, experimentation, or research. Their only tangible product is the report. If they are to have anything to show for their efforts, they must do a thorough job of reporting.

On the other hand, in some companies the report is only one kind of the writing being done, although reporting is the foundation for the other kinds. Manuals accompany machinery when it is sold; instruction books are given to repairmen; brochures are provided for salesmen.

Many important industrial and research organizations nowadays place so much value on their technical writing that they maintain separate editorial departments. Several well-known firms of consulting engineers have technical publication staffs which work with industrial organizations on the publication of reports and other technical material.

Technical reporting has achieved a recognized position of importance in our highly technological world.

1.2 The Importance of Proficiency in Technical Reporting

In many engineering organizations, particularly those doing experimental work or research, the young employee's chief communication with his superiors is through his written (or oral) reports. Often the supervisor has no other criterion by which to judge an employee's work.

Every technical school receives letters from important industrial firms complaining about the quality of the technical reports produced by its graduates. These young men, we are told, are admirably grounded in the basic sciences, they are intelligent, they are capable of doing excellent work. But their education has left a serious gap: they are unable to describe clearly and succinctly what they have done. This inability exists, we believe, not so much because the engineering schools fail to offer instruction in this important subject, but because the students lack sufficient motivation to apply themselves to it.

We hope that this introduction, together with the practical approach of *Technical Reporting,* will persuade you to put real effort into the study of this subject. If you do, we believe that you will find it to be not only challenging, but even interesting.

2. IMPORTANT FUNDAMENTAL PRINCIPLES

2.1 Communication

Technical reporting is a specialized branch of the field of *communication*. Communication may be broadly defined as the transmission of information or ideas from one mind to other minds. Every communication—whether it is a love song or a telegram, a novel or an instruction book—should have (1) a specific purpose and (2) a specific audience. It should be carefully planned and constructed to fit both.

2.2 Specific Purpose

Some forms of communication may have as their primary aim to convey a feeling or an atmosphere, or to amuse, or even to stupefy or confuse. But every technical communication has one certain clear purpose: *to convey information and ideas accurately and efficiently*. This objective requires that the communication be: (1) as *clear* as possible; (2) as *brief* as possible; and (3) as *easy to understand* as possible. If it can be made at the same time pleasant, or perhaps striking or forceful, all well and good. But these considerations and all others are secondary to the primary objectives of accuracy and efficiency.

Ways of achieving these ends will be the subject of a major portion of *Technical Reporting*.

2.3 Specific Audience

Any communication, if it is to be effective and efficient, must be designed for the needs and the understanding of a specific reader or group of readers. It must neither be beyond their powers of comprehension nor so far beneath their level of competence as to bore them and thus lose them. The successful comic book is easily followed by a moron; on the other hand, the treatise on operator theory in integral equations should not discourage its readers by including an extended discussion of Euclidean geometry.

The expected audience of a technical communication determines the treatment of several factors.

2.3.1 Background Information

Are the people who will see or hear this report familiar with the general field, or do they need extensive general orientation? Are they familiar with the circumstances of the present case, or do they need briefing? How much background information must you supply them? Always err on the side of giving them too much.

2.3.2 Technical Level

What is the technical training of your audience? They may be experts in your own field; they may have general scientific training but a specialization different from yours; or they may be laymen. Correspondingly, you may be able to take for granted the most advanced knowledge of the ideas and vocabulary of your own field; you may have to explain only specialized ideas or terms; or you may have to explain fully every concept that transcends the knowledge of the man on the street. Can you use differential equations in presenting your ideas, or must you restrict yourself to algebra? Or must you avoid the use of equations entirely?

Unfortunately the answers to these questions are often far from clear-cut. Many communications go to mixed audiences, perhaps widely mixed. A compromise treatment is called for, one aimed at the less-informed members of your audience rather than the better-informed.

But don't let the frequent need for compromise prevent you from always trying to determine the nature of your expected audience and fit-
ting your presentation to them just as closely as you can.

2.4 A Framework for the Parts

A highly important principle of technical reporting has been stated
so well by Professor Lynwood S. Bryant of the Massachusetts Institute
of Technology that we present it in his words:

> *The first thing an observer needs when he is confronted with a
> strange machine (or a strange concept) is a clear idea of the essence
> and function and purpose of the whole, considered as a unit. He
> needs an intelligible whole to fit the parts into as they are described.
> This simple psychological need of the reader is sometimes over-
> looked by the technical writer who has been so absorbed in details
> that he forgets to write down the main purpose of his design. A list
> of parts is not a substitute for a definition. The psychologically cor-
> rect place for it is after, not before, the definition.*

Thus, when you are writing about an investigation or an experiment,
start out by stating its general nature and its purpose. When you are
describing an apparatus or a machine, tell your reader about its fundamental character and its over-all arrangement before you mention any
details. When you are setting forth a theory, state its general purport
before you start deriving equations.

In short, before you plunge into any discourse, *tell your audience
what it's all about.*

Here is an example of the obscurity that results when an exposition
begins by describing parts rather than essentials. The left-hand column
contains the opening paragraphs of a student report on "The Efficiency
of a 24-Inch Cyclone." The right-hand column contains a suggested
revision in which the only change is an alteration of the sentence order.

Original Example	Suggested Revision
A cyclone collector is an apparatus used for the collection of dust particles entrained in gas. The body of the cy-	A cyclone collector is an apparatus used for the collection of dust particles entrained in gas. As the gas is drawn

Original Example	Suggested Revision

clone is a cylinder surmounting an inverted cone. The gas inlet is a rectangular pipe entering tangential to the body of the cyclone; the gas outlet is an inner concentric cylinder extending down into the body. The outlet for deposited dust is at the bottom of the cone.

As the gas is drawn through the cyclone, the structure of the cyclone imparts a rapid swirling motion to it. The exact nature of the process by which the cyclone pulls the dust out of the gas is not known, but it is thought to depend on the centrifugal force on the dust particles in the rapidly swirling gas.

through the cyclone, the structure of the cyclone imparts a rapid swirling motion to it. The exact nature of the process by which the cyclone pulls the dust out of the gas is not known, but it is thought to depend on the centrifugal force on the dust particles in the rapidly swirling gas.

The body of the cyclone is a cylinder surmounting an inverted cone. The gas inlet is a rectangular pipe entering tangential to the body of the cyclone; the gas outlet is an inner concentric cylinder extending down into the body. The outlet for deposited dust is at the bottom of the cone.

Or again:

Spot-test Analysis. The great value in the use of spot tests lies in the saving in time and materials; they are used where the supply of the material to be tested is small or where quick analysis is vital, as in process control. The amounts of test material used are very small, often only one drop. Spot tests are frequently used in the macro or micro schemes of analysis where identification would normally be poor. A fairly high degree of skill and some special apparatus are necessary in spot-test analysis.

Reactions are carried out on filter paper or on spot plates, microcrucibles, centrifuge cones, and micro test tubes. Many effects are used as aids in analysis, such as the capillary properties of filter paper, adsorption, catalyzed reactions, and fluorescence.

Spot-test Analysis. Spot tests are individual tests for single elements made on a single drop in the form of a spot on filter paper, a spot plate, a microcrucible, a centrifuge cone, or a micro test tube. Many effects are used as aids in analysis, such as the capillary properties of filter paper, adsorption, catalyzed reactions, and fluorescence.

The great value in the use of spot tests lies in the saving in time and materials; they are used where the supply of material to be tested is small or where quick analysis is vital, as in process control. Spot tests are frequently used in the macro or micro schemes of analysis where identification would normally be poor. A fairly high degree of skill and some special apparatus are necessary in spot-test analysis.

A more sophisticated example—and perhaps a more convincing one—comes from a leaflet entitled *United States Government Grants, Program Year 1951–1952; Manual of Procedures and Policies,* issued by the Institute of International Education. These are the opening two paragraphs:

1. Administration of the Program

The Secretary of State is responsible to Congress for the administration of Public Law 584, 79th Congress (the Fulbright Act). For the purpose of selecting recipients of awards and of supervising the exchange program, a Board of Foreign Scholarships, as provided by the Act, was appointed by the President. The Board of Foreign Scholarships makes the final selection of all grantees both foreign and American. The Institute of International Education has been requested by the Department of State and by the Board to aid in the operation of the student portion of the program, to publicize announcements concerning opportunities, to receive applications from American graduate students and to assist in the preliminary selection of applicants for student awards. The Institute of International Education also assists in raising dollar support for the tuition and maintenance in the United States of foreign students, recipients of travel grants under the Fulbright Act, and in arranging academic connections for them.

There are three other cooperating agencies concerned with the operation of the program. The Conference Board of Associated Research Councils was designated by the Department of State and the Board of Foreign Scholarships to assist in the preliminary selection of applicants for advanced research or teaching in foreign universities. The United States Office of Education has the responsibility for the preliminary selection of applicants for teaching in national primary and secondary schools abroad. The American Council on Education is responsible for the preliminary selection of applicants for teaching in American primary and secondary schools abroad.

Now, don't you want to know what the program *is* before you are told how it is administered? If you read through to page 6 of the leaflet, you come upon a sentence that begins to tell you:

The broad purpose of the Fulbright Act is to foster the growth of international understanding by providing opportunity for representative Americans to live and study abroad for an academic year.

Contrast this order of presentation with another contained in the same publication. On page 15 is a "Sample Press Release":

Opportunities for more than 600 Americans to undertake graduate study or research abroad during the 1951–52 academic year under the terms of the Fulbright Act have been announced by the Department of State. Countries in which study grants are available are Australia, Austria, Belgium, Burma, Egypt, France, Greece, India, Iran, Italy, the Netherlands, New Zealand, Norway, the Philippines, Thailand, Turkey and the United Kingdom.

The awards will enable students in all fields of graduate work and those with specialized research projects to study in foreign institutions and universities under renowned professors and specialists. Grants also are available to students with records of accomplishment in such fields as music, art, architecture, and drama. A few opportunities in workers' education and social work are provided in the United Kingdom.

The grants are made under Public Law 584, 79th Congress, the Fulbright Act, which authorizes the Department of State to use certain foreign currencies and credits acquired through the sale of surplus property abroad for programs of educational exchange with other nations. Grants are normally made for one academic year and generally include round trip transportation, tuition or a stipend, a living allowance and a small amount for necessary books and equipment. All grants under the Act are made in foreign currencies.

Don't you get a clearer picture and an easier one to assimilate when the broad, basic definition comes first? After this orientation, you are ready to be told about the administration of the program.

The emphasis and the repetition accorded to this principle is by design. It is of paramount importance. Remember: before you plunge into any discourse, *tell your audience what it's all about.*

2.5 Emphasis of the Significant

Closely related to the ideas of Sec. 2.4 is a fault found in technical reports perhaps more commonly than any other: the burial of the meat —the really important and significant ideas—under a mass of details. The reason for this failing is inherent in the nature of technical work. Before he finishes a task, the technical worker is thoroughly familiar with the main line of thought—the purpose and the method of attack. From day to day he has been coping with a lot of smaller problems, many of them probably routine and tedious. Consequently, when he sets about reporting on his work or his investigation, he talks primarily about the little problems that have occupied so much of his time and attention.

It is scarcely necessary to tell the engineer and the scientist how important it is to get the main points out in the open so that they will be seen and recognized and acted on. But it does seem in order to warn him that he must usually make a conscious, planned effort to keep his key ideas uncovered.

The remainder of Sec. 2.5 is devoted to some specific devices for making the important material stand out. In addition, practically all of the principles propounded in the rest of this book will help you to accomplish the same vital end.

2.5.1 Prominent Position

Perhaps the most fundamental way of making an idea stand out is to put it in a prominent position. The most prominent position in any report or paper is the very beginning. Even though you have not yet led up to it logically, you can often put across your major thesis most effectively by stating it right at the start and later supplying support for it.

A secondary prominent position is the end, particularly in a short communication. In a longer report or paper—we may as well face it—your reader may never get to the end.

Some specific suggestions for emphasis by position are given in Chapters 6 and 7, which discuss the structure of reports.

2.5.2 Elimination of Detail

One sure way to stress important information is to *remove* unessential material. Perhaps you can relegate it to the wastebasket, a difficult thing to do to the product of your toil.

On the other hand, you may need to include a lot of details for record purposes. If you do, you can usually put them into an appendix, leaving your main discourse uncluttered.

Ways of eliminating material are discussed more fully in Sec. 2.6; the function of the appendix is described in Sec. 7.4.

2.5.3 Elimination of Words

The clearing away of superfluous words almost always allows more light to reach what is left; see Sec. 13.3.

2.5.4 Liberal Use of Subheads

The great value of subheads for several purposes is discussed in detail in Sec. 2.8. One of their important functions is to announce and call attention to key material.

2.5.5 Repetition

Psychologists tell us that children learn by repeated experience. The same process works on even the sophisticated and highly educated scientist or engineer. If you want to be sure that an idea does not fade into the background, repeat it. Say it over and over. If you can say it in a different way each time, the repetition will be subtle and therefore palatable; but don't shy away from even bald, frank repetition if your point is important enough to warrant it.

2.5.6 Visual Aids and Tables

Visual aids—graphs, curves, drawings, diagrams, photographs—often present information in a striking and efficient manner.   They can be used to reinforce and emphasize key ideas.

The various visual aids, and tables, can themselves suffer the fault of hiding the significant behind a maze of unimportant detail.   Ways of making them bold and clear are described in Chapters 17 and 18.

2.5.7 Typography

Capital letters, larger type size, boldface, and italics are all effective means of emphasis *if not overused*.   Of these, only capital letters and italics (underlining) are available on the typewriter.

2.5.8 Specific Mention

It is all right to be explicit and say "This is a particularly important point," or "This is an important part of the report."   Such statements may be made along with the material they refer to, or they may be made separately in a letter of transmittal or preface.

2.6 How to Be Brief

Brevity may be achieved in two different ways: one is to skim over all the material at hand; the other is to cull out the insignificant and treat the significant exhaustively.   This culling process is not to be confused with suppression of data in order to color conclusions, a device that is not practiced by any self-respecting engineer or scientist.

Consider the two bar charts of Fig. 1, page 14.

Let us say that each bar represents the treatment of one factor in a paper you have written.   A 100-percent complete coverage means that you have supplied so much information that the reader can understand you with a minimum of work on his part—without having to fill in any gaps or steps.

Now suppose that your first draft of the paper is obviously much too long—let us say twice too long. You must remove half of your draft.

You can conceivably remove steps and particulars from the treatment of each of your five factors until they are each just half as long as originally—and each just 50-percent complete. The result is depicted in Fig. 1a.

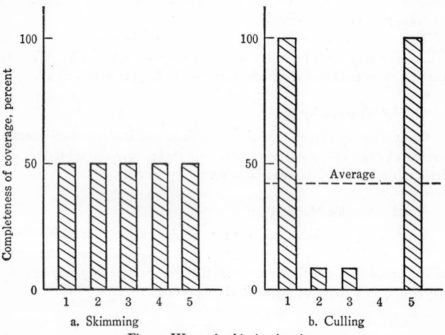

Fig. 1. Ways of achieving brevity

What effect does this boiling-down have on your reader? Each of your five factors is described fully enough to make him try to understand it. Yet he must go to endless work to fill in the information you have withheld from him. If he is very curious about your subject, he will go through with this tedious process, with a large expenditure of effort and great annoyance. But more likely he will give the whole thing up as a bad job and turn to some easier and pleasanter task.

On the other hand, suppose you appraise your five factors carefully. You decide that factor 4 is trivial and can be thrown out without serious loss. Factors 2 and 3 should be very briefly mentioned. And factors 1 and 5 are really significant, deserving of 100-percent coverage. Again, as shown in Fig. 1b, the average coverage, and thus the total length, is about half the original.

And now what of your reader? Your brief mention of factors 2 and 3 does not stimulate him to fill in some gaps and find out all about them; he is willing to accept them on your say-so. Factor 4 is of course no worry to him at all. And the significant factors 1 and 5 he understands fully and with a minimum of work on his part.

Only two levels of treatment are readily accepted by most people: the very complete and the very brief. As illustrated in the following short example, the great middle ground of partial treatment tickles the curiosity, then annoys or baffles.

> Many metals are extracted from their ores by a process known as smelting. For example, iron ore is placed in blast furnaces with coke and limestone. The ore is heated, reducing the metal to the free and molten state. The molten iron is poured into molds.

The reader unfamiliar with the smelting of iron ore is left wondering how the coke and limestone enter into this process. The writer should have either explained why they are put into the furnaces with the ore, or not mentioned them at all.

Since most of the readers of this book will be college students, we should like to call attention to a serious departure of the usual college *theme, term paper,* or *laboratory report* from the principles of good technical reporting we have discussed up to this point. The primary purpose of these college papers is usually not to transmit some information to a specific audience; it is, rather, to show the instructor that the writer has gained some knowledge. The paper is addressed to somebody who already has the knowledge, and who is thus by no means a typical audience. To make sure that they omit no pertinent information, the writers of college themes and papers tend to include every detail they can lay their hands on, rather than to cull out the unimportant and the insignificant.

Consequently most college papers do not furnish good practice in technical communication. The provision of realistic reporting assignments for technical students usually requires a carefully planned program of cooperation between the English department and the several professional departments.

2.7 Organization

Unfortunately, there is no neat formula for the organization of technical reports. Each report must be organized to fit its own subject, its own purpose, its own audience. But a few general principles apply to most technical communications.

2.7.1 Logical Progression toward Conclusions

Almost every technical report aims to bring its reader to certain conclusions. These conclusions need not be of the conventional, formal variety such as "It is concluded that the piston failed because of an inclusion in the casting." They may be simply that "No conclusions are warranted by the data developed in this study." But in general, the information you present in technical reports is intended to bring your reader to some sort of a conclusion.

Thus the material in any report or paper should be presented in an order that leads logically toward a conclusion or conclusions. This does not mean, of course, that everything in a lengthy report will aim at one final climax; the various sections of the report are organized so that each of them has its logical conclusions.

Application of this rule might seem to relegate the conclusions—usually the most important ideas in a report—to a position of relative obscurity, buried under pages of data. To make sure that the conclusions are not overlooked by even the busiest or most hurried reader, most present-day technical reports and papers carry a statement (or a restatement) of the important conclusions at the very beginning. See Secs. 6.1, 7.2.4, and 7.3.

2.7.2 Topical *vs.* Chronological

The two basic approaches for any exposition are the *chronological* and the *topical*. Except for the purely historical subject—and sometimes even for it—the topical treatment is preferable in technical reporting. By and large, your reader wants to know what you investigated and what you found out—he wants to know why you did things and how you did them—rather than the story of your investigation.

Of course, some chronology may be entirely appropriate. The events leading up to an investigation may show why you have undertaken it, or a procedure may appear more sensible and more logical if you describe the order of the steps you went through.

Although you may have occasion to mix some chronology into your treatment, the topical approach will usually be basically the more suitable one.

2.7.3 The Three Parts

Almost every technical communication should have three functional elements. This does not mean that it should be divided by boundaries into three distinct parts. But functionally it should have a beginning, a middle, and an end. Too many technical reporters devote so much of their attention to the middle that they slight the beginning and the end, both of which are very important.

The beginning is often called the *Introduction,* although a more specific title is preferable (see Sec. 7.2.2). This beginning orients the reader. It supplies him with background material, so that he will see how the subject of the paper fits into the general scheme of things. It helps to supply the framework called for in Sec. 2.4. It prepares the reader for the main presentation of information—the middle.

The middle is usually the longest part of the report. It can be organized in many different ways; some of them are discussed in Sec. 7.2.

The end is sometimes labeled *Conclusions,* although again a more specific title is preferable. It brings together the various subjects that have been discussed and shows their relationships with each other and with broader fields. It leaves the reader with some thoughts about the main subject under discussion, rather than merely about one phase of it. This end section makes the exposition come to a logical and an obvious termination, rather than simply stop on a note of detail. It ties a string around the bundle.

2.8 Subheadings

The importance of subheadings can hardly be overestimated. You will seldom see too many of them in a technical report or paper; very often, too few. They serve a number of vital functions.

2.8.1 A Help to the Reader

(1) Subheads make the structure of the exposition apparent. They help to supply the reader with that framework on which to fasten the parts.

(2) Subheads serve as convenient and efficient signposts. They let the reader know that he has reached the end of one subject and is about to begin a new one. Two alternatives occur if this information is not supplied by subheads: either the writer supplies it in sentence form, as part of his exposition; or the reader is left to discover belatedly that he has left one subject and embarked upon a new one. The first of these alternatives wastes the reader's time; the second wastes his time and temporarily mystifies him besides.

(3) The reader may have to interrupt his reading to answer the telephone or speak to a colleague or go to lunch. When he returns to an exposition that has a generous supply of subheads, he has to go back only a few paragraphs to the last subhead to pick up the thread of the discourse. But when he returns to an exposition with few subheads or none, he may have to backtrack for several pages before he can proceed again.

(4) When he is studying a long or complicated exposition, the reader may have to go back and reread in order to refresh his memory or to cast new light on a subject only partially understood at first. He can find the material he is looking for very much more easily if he is supplied with subheads.

(5) The mind, like the stomach, can assimilate material more easily if it is broken down into chunks of digestible size before it is swallowed. Subheads perform this chewing function very efficiently.

2.8.2 A Help to the Writer

(1) The logical system of subheads, by acting as an outline, keeps the writer in clear channels. (The addition of subheads to an exposition that did not originally have them often brings to light repetition or other illogical organization.)

(2) The use of subheads is a particularly easy way of supplying the transitions, or connective tissue, needed to make any discourse smooth and unified.

(3) Subheads make it easier to refer to specific parts of a report or paper.

Obviously, the longer and more complex any exposition, the more it needs subheads. But even the very short report can often be clarified and made easier for the reader if it is broken up by subheads. A half-page, two-paragraph memorandum reproduced in Sec. 20.2.2 is certainly helped by the presence of two subheads.

2.9 Consistency

The technical report should be thoroughly consistent in every phase. If you label a point Q on a drawing but call it q in the text, you will confuse and mislead your reader. If you refer to a part at one moment as a pivot and at the next as a pin, he may think you are talking about two different objects.

A certain paper on the design of an electrical measuring instrument discussed the types of circuits that might be suitable. In various parts of the discussion the following types were mentioned: (1) condenser-resistor, (2) resistor-inductance, (3) capacitance-resistance, (4) resistance-condenser, (5) inductance-resistance. The thoughtful reader can reduce these to two kinds of circuits and can pick a consistent pair of terms for them—*capacitance-resistance* and *inductance-resistance*. But he should not be put to this trouble. (As a matter of fact, the paper from which this example was taken used still another term—the ambiguous *reactance-resistance*—to mean inductance-resistance.)

A particularly troublesome inconsistency is a change in units of measurement. For instance, in the two reports on a pair of related tests performed at a commercial laboratory, a wear rate was given first in thousandths of an inch per 1000 miles, then in thousandths of an inch per 10,000 miles. Such a discrepancy can cause serious misapprehension on the part of a casual reader. Similarly, curves that are to be compared should be plotted to the same scales.

Perhaps less serious than inconsistencies in nomenclature or units but still troublesome and annoying to the reader are inconsistencies in abbreviation, hyphenation, capitalization, or use of numerals. At the very least, the reader pauses to question the significance of the variation that has no significance. You owe it to him to reread your manuscript very

carefully to see that you have been consistent in even the smallest mechanical details.   Sometimes even a consistent small error is preferable
to vacillation between a correct form and an incorrect form.

2.10 Specific Identification

You can save your reader a lot of trouble by making every reference
and every statement just as specific as possible.   In the table below are
some nonspecific statements with their specific counterparts.   Notice
how much more helpful the entries in the *Specific* column would be to
any reader.

Nonspecific	Specific
As described elsewhere in this report . . .	As described on page 6 . . .
These details are shown in the figure.	These details are shown in the center portion of Fig. 8.
Fuel consumption was 15 percent less in Test 12–4Y than in Test 12–3Z.	The Rumbler 8 consumed 15 percent less fuel than the Wonder 6.
The first of these methods is the simplest . . .	Cupellation is the simplest of these methods.
Fig. 2 summarizes the picture with respect to dealers.	Fig. 2 shows the distribution of retail volume, wholesale volume, and number of outlets among dealerships of various sizes.
If the transaction with Mr. Smith cannot be effected . . .	If Mr. Smith does not buy the bulldozer . . .

2.11 Expression of Opinion

In an effort to stress the importance of accuracy and objectivity in
technical reporting, some instructors convey the idea to their students
that the technical report must present only facts, never opinion.   However, engineers and scientists are employed not only to discover facts,
but also to make deductions from those facts and to make decisions
based on them.   Therefore the technical report must often present the
judgments and opinions of its writer or his organization.

Your duty is not to refrain from expressing opinion; it is rather to tell your reader very certainly what you are doing whenever you have occasion to introduce opinion into your reporting. Of course your opinion should be based as soundly as possible on demonstrated facts, and it should be as impartial as you can make it. But no matter how objective you think you have been, whenever you express an opinion, tell your reader. Some ways of fulfilling this obligation are discussed in Sec. 13.13.

2.12 Conclusions and Recommendations

Some young engineers are so unsure of themselves that they hesitate to draw conclusions or make recommendations on the basis of their observations. Indeed, in some organizations only the supervisors or executives are permitted to formulate conclusions and recommendations. But unless you have been told specifically that you are to report only observed facts and that you are not to make deductions from these facts, your comments and conclusions will probably be welcomed by your superiors. But be sure never to draw conclusions on the basis of numerical differences that are not significant or that are smaller than the probable error of measurement. Do not be afraid to make the conclusion "No conclusions are warranted by the results of this investigation."

2.13 Date

The date is a seemingly insignificant item that should go on every written record or report. No matter whether it is a highly polished formal report, a memorandum, or a page in a laboratory notebook, it should be dated. No matter what firm you work for or what forms they use, be sure to date everything you write. For it is often important to know which of two reports was written first, or when a certain practice was started or stopped, or when an action was taken. And of course the date is essential on any record of research or design work that may later become the basis for a patent application. Many a technical man has regretted afterward that he didn't date a memorandum that seemed trivial when it was being written. Remember: put the date on everything you write.

2.14 Titles

In the course of reporting on technical work, you will often have to write titles—titles not only of papers or reports, but also of drawings and diagrams, graphs and curve sheets, tables, and columns in the tables. Every title—no matter which of these categories it belongs to—should be just as short as possible yet still descriptive of its subject. The title of a report or paper should bring out the fundamental, over-all nature of the subject, and it should be as specific as possible without going into details. But sometimes the subject is so complex, or so limited, that it cannot be adequately described in a short title. In this event, a title plus subtitle is a useful combination: the brief main title serves as a convenient handle, while the subtitle furnishes specific limiting, qualifying, or explanatory information.

Titles in technical reporting seem to deviate from these ideals in both directions: an occasional title is so brief or so general that it does not sufficiently describe or limit its subject; a good many titles are so detailed that they obscure basic ideas. Here are some examples of faulty titles, with suggestions for their improvement:

Original Example	Suggested Revision
Aluminum Oxide	Aluminum Oxide: Physical Properties
Input Devices	Conversion of Shaft Position to Binary Number Code for a Digital Computer
Rumbler 6 Exhaust Valve Performance During Cycling Operation of a 300-Cubic-Inch Military Engine with Fuel Containing 5.0 ml Anti-K per Gallon and with S-L Synthetic Crankcase Lubricant	The Effect of S-L Synthetic Crankcase Lubricant on a Rumbler 6 Engine

Many reports carry titles encumbered by superfluous words that fall into a pattern: *Report on . . . , Study of . . . , Test of . . . , Investigation of . . .* , and so on. The information contained in these phrases is usually self-evident. If a report is put up and bound in the conventional way, it is quite obviously a report, and nobody is enlightened by the words *Report on* on its label. Similarly, does *Investigation of the Physical Properties of Aluminum Oxide* convey any information not contained in *Aluminum Oxide: Physical Properties?* Nobody is likely to report on these properties without first investigating them. Usually words of this pattern can simply be deleted from any title; occasionally they may be significant enough to be left in.

2.15 Test for an Effective Report

The foregoing sections of this chapter have suggested a number of basic principles for effective technical reporting. Most of these principles are equally applicable to written or oral communications, long or short ones, formal reports, informal reports, papers for the journals, or articles for the press.

We have now established enough of the criteria of good technical reporting to suggest a quick test for the effectiveness of any technical reporting job. When you have finished reading it (or hearing it), ask yourself *what is its central theme*. If you can answer this question readily, the report is probably a good one.

EXERCISES

1. Go to the library and obtain an industrial or research report. Make a check list of the important fundamental principles for preparing a report. Place them in a left-hand column. In the right-hand column, evaluate the report according to these principles.

2. Write a short account of two reports you have looked over. One of the reports should be an example of the chronological approach, the other of the topical approach.

3. Find examples, if possible, in existing reports of how the authors have handled the basic principle of stating the general nature and purpose of an investigation or an experiment. Report orally to the class on your study.

3. GENERAL PROCEDURE

People often ask how to go about writing a report or paper. Again, unfortunately, no formula is available: each person has his own work habits, and each subject imposes its own requirements. But a general order of procedure does seem worth suggesting.

3.1 Collection of Information or Data

The first requisite for good writing or good speaking is to have something to say. So the first step in every technical reporting job is the collection of data or the development of information.

In general, information comes from these sources: documentation, experimentation, observation, and logical thinking. It may be gathered in a laboratory or a library; it may come about through watching work being done; or it may be the product of logical thought processes in the mind of the writer.

When you are writing, you must learn to judge and evaluate your material. Certainly one of the first principles is to approach your material in a scientific manner. Because your emphasis will be on the material itself and not on any preconceived ideas, be ready to shift your point of view, and the scope of your writing, up to the time you put everything down in a first draft.

No matter what the source or nature of your facts, you can facilitate one of your early steps—the preparation of the outline—by recording the facts on cards, one topic to a card. Take complete and accurate notes as you go along, whether they come from the laboratory or the library. The usual practice is to put the data on cards of reasonable size (4 x 6 inches or 3 x 5 inches is handy). But remember that the most important single item in note taking is accuracy. Verify quotations, and especially figures, while the sources are available.

One way of recording data is to break your topics into reasonable subtopics and to list each of these on a card, starting at the top on the left side. The main portion of the card will then contain the information itself. How complete it is depends on how readily available your sources are. For example, if you cannot retain a source book, or if you cannot trust your memory beyond a certain time, your notations will have to be particularly complete; otherwise, scattered phrases may be enough. At the bottom of the card, cite the source, with page numbers if the note came from a document.

Here is what a note card might look like:

Causes of Fractures

    In the experiment cited, examination shows fractures probably caused by three kinds of corrosion—atmospheric, elevated temperature, intergranular.

E. E. Farrell. "Corrosion Resistance." *Iron* (June 1945), 62–65.

You would probably find the topic *Causes of Fractures* too large to continue using; in that case, it would be better to take notes under each of the subtopics: *atmospheric, elevated temperature, intergranular.*

    A word of caution about library research: When you are gathering information from the library, you should probably record it on your cards in outline or telegraphic style. This method will preclude the inadvertent plagiarism that might occur when you have later forgotten whether you copied or paraphrased full sentences.

You may have occasion to copy some passages verbatim, because you may want to quote an author's own words. Be sure to put prominent quotation marks on any cards that carry verbatim quotations.

Note cards, of course, will deal with other information besides that found in books. Speeches you have heard, material from interviews, digests of conferences, trips you have taken through factories—all of these can be reduced to a workable form by recording them on cards.

3.2 The Outline

If you use this system of topical note-taking, you are well on the way to making an outline. Because outlines result from a combination of what you already know about a subject and what you record on your note cards, very early in your writing you should draw up some kind of tentative outline.

If you are human, you will probably depart from the outline at one place or another when you come to do the writing. Setting ideas down on paper usually requires rigorous thinking that further clarifies them in your mind or sheds new light on them. You may have to revise your outline as you write.

But the outline is none the less a valuable tool. At the very least, it provides you with a starting point, serves as a general framework, and keeps you thinking along logical lines.

The longer the paper, the more you will need an outline; but even the short composition will be easier to write and clearer to read if you construct an outline before you set down a single sentence. The entire process of outlining, then, usually takes place in these four stages:

(1) A tentative outline is set up at the earliest possible time.

(2) Gathering of material continues and a topical card system is built up.

(3) Note cards are arranged and rearranged in the light of the tentative outline and the data compiled.

(4) A final outline is made and becomes the basis of the rough draft.

The function of the outline does not end with the writing of the text. The reader of a really well-planned report or paper should be able to detect the outline, at least its major divisions. Perhaps he can reconstruct it simply from the flow of topics; perhaps you will supply it for him by using your outline entries as subheadings in the final draft.

Some suggestions for arrangement of outline headings are given in Sec. 16.7.

3.3 Tabulation and Plotting of Data

Just as it is easier for the reader to grasp the significance of figures when they are tabulated or plotted, so it is for the author (see Chapters 17 and 18). Therefore, whenever you are writing about any subject that involves numerical data, you should probably tabulate or plot your figures before you start writing. This sequence of operations will help you to interpret your facts and to write about them clearly.

3.4 The Rough Draft

After you have constructed your outline, *write a rough draft just as quickly and just as consecutively as you can,* paying little attention to niceties of language. Leave plenty of space between lines for subsequent revision. *Concentrate on a smooth and connected presentation.* You may have to go back momentarily and reread sections or even revise them slightly to keep your approach consistent, but save the major polishing job for later.

Not everyone will be able to use this method: some people seem to find it necessary to weigh every word before they put it down. But if your habits of mind permit you to take this advice, it will probably help you to produce integrated, coherent papers and reports.

3.5 Revision and Polishing

Have you ever read a letter or a paper that you yourself wrote a year or two previously? Did you notice how objectively you were able to view it, as if you were reading the writing of someone else? Perhaps you were pleased with the general effect of your brain child; but very likely you came upon passages that were not entirely clear because of gaps in the information supplied, or you were struck with awkward repetition of words, or you noticed other matters that you would change if you had the job to do over again.

When you read a passage right after you have written it, your complete familiarity with the subject enables you to fill in the gaps that you have left in your exposition. But in time these pieces of the puzzle escape from your mind, and then you, as a reader, are confronted with the same problems that a stranger would be.

Therefore you should *let as much time as possible elapse between the composition of the rough draft and the revision-and-polishing job.* (We hasten to point out that this procedure entails writing the rough draft earlier, rather than the final draft later.)

Professor Douglas H. Washburn of Rensselaer Polytechnic Institute has compiled a check list to be used in revising a manuscript.

In part, he offers these suggestions for revising, polishing, and evaluating your rough draft:

(1) State in a single sentence what you wish the reader to retain. Write this sentence out. It is intended to define the central communication you wish to achieve and to which all the details are subordinate.

(2) Read the draft straight through in order to decide in what respects it needs to be revised.

(3) Make up your mind in which of the following ways you wish to revise:

    (a) Shorten the manuscript.

    (b) Increase the readability.

    (c) Make the organization more effective.

    (d) Make a closer tie-in with illustration.

(a) To shorten the manuscript, look for:

Circumlocutions: *"In the month of May* production reached a peak." (See Sec. 13.3.2.)

Superfluous words: "The engine *which has been equipped* with a governor . . ." (See Sec. 13.3.1.)

Phrases to be reduced to single adjectives or adverbs: "The sample *with the coat of red* paint . . ."

Adjectives or adverbs the opposite of which would be unlikely in the context: "One *possible* plan would be to . . ."

Ideas or facts which do not contribute to the main part of your writing, as defined in the single sentence.

Examples demonstrating points already made clear.

(b) To increase readability:

Break up long sentences. (See Sec. 13.5.2.)
Find common words to substitute for your more unusual terms. (See Sec. 13.2.2.)
Use more headings. (See Sec. 2.8.)
Place your main points in conspicuous positions. (See Sec. 2.5.1.)
Show your reader how the subject being discussed affects him.

(c) To make your organization more effective:

Check your rough draft against your outline.
Make certain that your table of contents is logically arranged.
Check your paragraphs to see that they are logically constructed and deal with one topic at a time.

(d) To make a closer tie-in with illustrations:

Make sure that each illustration is placed immediately after the first reference to it in the text. (See Sec. 18.3.)
Replace such stock phrases as "See Fig. 96" with a discussion of the illustration to guide the reader to a complete understanding of the text-illustration relationship.

The amount of polishing required depends on the writer's ability to say things well the first time and also on the use to which the composition will be put. A newspaper article or a memorandum cannot be delayed for the overhauling that you would accord an article for one of the technical journals, nor is it likely to be worthy of such effort.

Many experienced writers go slowly and painstakingly through several drafts before they are satisfied to release any serious piece of writing for publication. Dull as the task may sometimes seem, you should by all means do a thorough job of revising and polishing everything you write for more than casual or transitory purposes.

3.6 Typing

After final revision, your report or paper will be typed. You may have to do this task yourself; you may be fortunate enough to have a wife who will do it for you; or you may be in an organization that supplies stenographic service. The typed copy may be the end product of your labor, or it may be the basis for reproduction of your opus in quantity. (Methods of reproduction are described in Sec. 16.11.) In either event it should be as accurate and as neat as it can possibly be made.

3.7 Proofreading

If you do your own typing, you will probably make typographical errors. If you have your typing done by someone else, even a professional stenographer, remember that she has probably copied much of your manuscript without understanding what she was typing, particularly if your treatment is highly technical or mathematical. This kind of mechanical copying is likely to lead to errors even by a highly skilled typist.

Therefore, no matter who has typed your final copy, it will probably contain mistakes. The only way to eliminate all of them is for you yourself to do a thorough job of proofreading.

You owe this admittedly tedious chore to yourself and to your readers. Remember that it is not only the major blunder that is confusing or misleading; the little typographical error can distort or even contradict your meaning. Your reader should never be put to the trouble of straightening out even a fairly obvious slip; and you should preserve your reputation for accuracy and precision by seeing that he never has to.

4. TECHNICAL DESCRIPTION

Frequently in technical reporting you must describe not only the complete project but also machines with which you worked, processes within the larger framework, and theories involving both machines and processes.

4.1 Description of Machines

A machine is a working object; consequently you must show the reader not only what it is, but what it does. Give him a general statement incorporating these two points to place the device in functional surroundings.

You may have to describe the theory or principle upon which the machine is built. In general, you can assume that the specialist will be familiar with the principles of machines that are modifications of those already in use; that the background principles of radically new machines should be extensively explained; and that for the more general reader a discussion of theory should be omitted.

Unless you are describing an extremely simple machine, do not take up details before you have given a broad, over-all description (see Sec.

2.4). It is easy for the reader to get misconceptions about size, shape, color, and other physical characteristics.

Details should be described in a systematic manner according to some logical order. One possible order is by *function;* that is, the parts of a machine are described in the order in which they function when the machine is put in motion.

Sometimes an order of *importance* is more logical. Although a machine usually depends on all its parts, some of these may be more important than others because they represent new ideas put into practice, or because certain primary operations depend on them. Occasionally you will be faced with the fact that two or more parts operate at the same time. For any of these reasons, you may have to fall back on *importance* as a unifying principle.

A third logical order often used is *spatial.* The parts are described as you come to them. This may be from left to right, top to bottom, inside to outside.

4.2 Description of Processes

It is difficult to imagine a process that does not involve a machine or device of some kind. Therefore what has already been said about describing machines applies to processes. The major difference, however, between describing a machine and a process is that with a machine the emphasis is on the object that does the work, whereas with a process the emphasis is on the work itself. You must, therefore, take special care to see that the steps in a process are carefully explained and arranged. Your material will determine your method. As with machines, you can use an arrangement based on *function, importance,* or *space,* or combinations of these.

Sometimes there are several ways of carrying out the same process, and this is especially true with natural phenomena. Soil erosion will produce the same result, but the process in one locality may be quite different from that in another. In your description, then, determine if there are variations to the basic process. If so, they should be described. And it will clarify your writing if you end with a complete description of the product obtained or any other end result of the process.

4.3 Description of Theories

Theories are usually more difficult to describe than machines or processes. With machines and processes, the material is based largely on facts, and your primary purpose in describing them is to inform. But as soon as you start theorizing and try to answer the question "why," the element of probability will enter your writing, as well as conjecture and persuasion.

The description of a theory can start out like the description of a machine or process. But *importance* will be the key word. The reader will want to know why it is necessary for him to be given such basic and fundamental material. He will need to know the *application* of the theory to the main purpose of the report you are writing; and it may also be necessary to include something on *historical development* so that he can understand the theory in its proper perspective.

The main part of the description of a theory is usually arranged according to one of three plans, or combinations:

(1) A new theory may call for an arrangement based on *synthesis* —the assembling of facts one by one until they can be combined into a general, all-embracing statement. This arrangement is useful when you wish to lead the reader along the path which you yourself took in reaching a conclusion.

(2) For the clarification of a complicated idea, the *analytical* method may be useful. This approach is suitable when you find it practical to break a general statement into parts and to examine each of these in detail.

(3) For a reader who is almost totally unfamiliar with the material, a theory will be clarified by *comparison* or *analogy*. With this method you can describe new theories by relating them to others generally well known.

4.4 Variations in Description

As with all kinds of writing, the style and complexity of technical description depends on the reader for whom you are writing (see Sec. 2.3). Therefore, you may have to consider variations in the techniques we have already suggested.

In describing a machine for a layman, for example, it may be desirable to start out by explaining the ways in which the machine affects him. He may be interested in efficiency, in the newness of the device, or in its uniqueness. In other words, be particularly strong in *reader motivation* and personal appeal.

For such a reader, we should like to stress again the use of *analogy*. Analogy is an informal type of definition, using comparison and contrast. We recall reading an article on aircraft hydraulic systems in which, to quote the author, "The unloading valve in the pump acts like a policeman directing traffic." And in another place the author says: "In a basic hydraulic system it should be remembered that the pump is the most important part, just as the heart is the most important part of the human system."

For the layman you may have to use *dramatization* and *incident*. The description of a process in celestial navigation was most effectively pointed up by taking an imaginary character, John Doe, through the ordeal of being set adrift in mid-ocean and showing how he put to practical use his knowledge of celestial navigation.

The theory is sometimes complicated by the fact that you must not only describe it, you must persuade the reader to accept it. Here is where two principles of argumentation may enter your writing: (1) at the outset establish a framework for your arguments, defining the premise on which your arguments will be based and the *limits* you will set; and (2) *anticipate objections* which may arise in the mind of your reader. These objections are bound to appear if your subject is at all controversial; either admit their validity or prove their falsity before they become fixed in your reader's mind.

4.5 Suggested Outlines

The outlines below sum up our suggestions for basic descriptions of machines, processes, and theories:

Machines
(1) Nature and Function
(2) Theories and General Principles
(3) General Description

(4) Specific Description
    —by order of function
    —by order of importance
    —by order of spatial arrangement

Processes
(1) Nature and Function
(2) Theories and General Principles
(3) Materials and Machines Involved
(4) General Procedure
(5) Detailed Steps in the Process
(6) Variations in the Process
(7) End Result

Theories and Ideas
(1) Nature and Function
(2) Importance of the Idea
(3) Application
(4) Historical Development
(5) Description by
    —synthesis
    —analysis
    —comparison
(6) Summary

EXERCISES

1. A new machine called the Secret Recorder has recently been released to the public. As part of a manual of operation, the machine must be described. The data are as follows:

Trade name: Secret Recorder.
Manufactured by a well-established and dignified electronics corporation.
Product comes camouflaged in an average-sized leather briefcase, which may be opened, carried, or put down without revealing the fact that the recorder is in operation.
Dimensions: 16 x 12½ x 4½ inches.
Recording microphone is built in.
Unit operates entirely from batteries: the motor from five mercury batteries, the amplifier from standard dry cells.
There is a built-in preamplifier for headphone playback.

Unit records continuously for 90 minutes at a tape speed of $1\frac{7}{8}$ inches per second, using long-play tape.

A 5-inch reel, therefore, accommodates 3 hours of dual-tracking recording.

Recorded tape may be played back on any standard machine operating at $1\frac{7}{8}$ inches per second.

Rewinds electrically in 2 minutes.

Unit is in full-scale production.

Fidelity is high considering the small size.

Weight: $11\frac{3}{4}$ pounds.

Manufacturer indicates that the product is excellent for investigative work.

Describe the machine for the consumer, assuming that a manual of use will follow your instructions.

2. The Palmer Casting Corporation of Fletcher, California, has produced an unusual steel shaft to be used in a new wind tunnel being built at the Burbank Engineering Center, Telemanee, Wisconsin.

You have been given the following information:

Steel shaft connects wind-tunnel motors to compressors of the transonic tunnel.

Weight: 50 tons.

Length: 25 feet.

Diameter: 2.5 feet.

Diameter of coupling: 5.5 feet.

Power carried from four motors (two of these larger than any previously built for the purpose).

Vibration: less than 0.001 inch.

Shaft floated in oil on bearings.

Can be turned by one hand pushing on brake wheel.

Write a description of the piece of machinery, to be used in a technical magazine.

3. For a manual of operation, it is often necessary to describe a machine or device before you tell someone how to use it. In 200 words or less, describe such a machine, assuming that a set of instructions will follow.

4. Students working in laboratories for the first time may be confused by the equipment that they must use. Describe a piece of laboratory equipment. Assume that the description will later be posted near the equipment itself.

5. For your class describe a process upon which you have been working in the laboratory.

6. Assume that you manufacture a machine for commercial use.

Your salesmen require a description of the machine for demonstration purposes. Write such a description for this specific group.

7. Describe a process as it occurs in nature. Write it first for technical readers; then adapt it if necessary for semitechnical readers.

8. Assume that you have been asked to write portions of a high school text on general science. Your contribution in each case is to be the description of a theory that is to be followed by a section on practical applications and demonstrations. Write the theory section for one item, using a maximum of 300 words.

9. In writing technical advertising for technical magazines, the copy writer must frequently describe machines, processes, and theories in a few words. Decide on the item you will advertise. Write about 100 words of technical description to be incorporated in a one-page advertisement.

PART II

THE REPORT

5. REPORTS—GENERAL

5.1 Types of Reports

Some textbooks on technical writing divide written reports into a large number of carefully distinguished classifications. They may list as distinct types information reports, periodic reports, progress reports, examination reports, and recommendation reports. They may separate letters into letters of inquiry, answers to inquiries, letters of instruction, and letters of transmittal. They may make distinctions between descriptive reports, analytic reports, evaluative reports, and many others.

You will notice that these listings classify the reports by their subject matter rather than by their form. Now we believe that in general all technical reports have the same functions to fulfill and that they are governed by the same principles no matter what their subject. For instance, suppose you were writing a report on the metallurgical analysis of a failed casting. Perhaps you were told simply to determine the cause of failure, and stop there. Your report would then be an "analytical" report. On the other hand, you might have been told to make recommendations about foundry practice to eliminate such failures in future castings. In this case, your report would be a "recommendation" report.

But how would these two reports differ? Only in the presence or absence of the recommendations. Would they be essentially different? Would your general approach and your problems in writing them be any different? We believe not.

Therefore in *Technical Reporting,* except in connection with a few short reports, we shall not classify reports by their subject matter, but by their form; and the two broad classifications we shall make are overlapping and far from rigid. They are (1) the long or formal report and (2) the short or informal report.

Whether a report is long or short, it should fulfill the requirements discussed in Chapter 2: it should orient the reader and provide him with a framework on which to hang the parts, and then it should transmit its information to him clearly and efficiently. Whether it is long or short, it will do these things better if it has been prepared in accordance with the principles presented in Chapter 2 and Chapters 13–18.

But the longer a report, the more it needs (1) a sturdy and convenient binding and (2) an obvious, formal organization, with its parts clearly labeled and listed. It is these two comparatively superficial differences that distinguish the formal report from the informal report. The formal report (Chapter 7) is usually bound in a cardboard cover, or perhaps even in a cloth binding. It is usually divided into separate main sections, each beginning on a new page, and it has a table of contents. The informal report (Chapter 6) is usually simply stapled together, with no cover. It is likely to be loosely divided by means of informal subheadings rather than separated into major sections, and if it is short it can get along without a table of contents. But some informal reports are quite highly organized, with forewords, summaries, tables of contents, and other parts that are usually associated with more formal documents. Thus the formal report may sometimes be differentiated from the informal only by the presence of a cover and a title page.

The length criterion does not establish a line of demarcation between formal and informal reports, either. Ten pages might serve as an arbitrary dividing line between the long or formal report and the short or informal report. Yet we have seen formal, bound reports with no more than three pages of text, and informal, unbound reports of more than fifty pages. The decision whether to make a report formal or informal depends not only on its length, but also on the readers for whom it is intended, and how much of an impression you wish to make on them; the finality of the judgments in it; and the time available for its preparation.

So far we have mentioned only *reports,* formal and informal (letters are included under informal reports in Chapter 6). In addition, *Technical Reporting* discusses three other sorts of communications—technical papers and articles in Chapter 10, instructions in Chapter 11, and oral reports in Chapter 12.

5.2 Forms of Reports

In Chapters 6 and 7 you will find some suggestions for the form, or makeup, of various kinds of reports and letters and their headings, and in Appendix Sec. 20.2 you will find reproductions of reports and letters that illustrate them. These forms have actually been used by successful organizations, and they are clear and effective. *But we wish to emphasize that they are simply examples from a wide choice of acceptable forms. The organization for which you work will very likely have its own standardized forms and headings for various written communications. Unless you can convince your superiors that these forms should be changed, you will of course abide by the local rules, even though they differ from the suggestions in this book.*

6. INFORMAL REPORTS

6.1 General Principles

Chapter 5 pointed out some of the ways in which informal reports differ from formal reports. In general, informal reports are less finished—less polished—than formal reports; they are appropriate for informal situations. For our purposes we can divide informal reports into two general classifications: (1) the short-form report or memo report, discussed in Sec. 6.2, and (2) the letter report, discussed in Sec. 6.3.

The informal report—particularly if it is short—does not need the explicit formal organization of the formal report. But reports of all kinds have essentially the same job to do, so that they need the same functional elements if not the same outward form. Thus three features regularly associated with formal reports will usually help even the short informal report to transmit information efficiently:

(1) An early statement of the problem or purpose. Even when a man is generally familiar with a situation, he needs some introduction —a leading-in—before he is ready to plunge into it. Your boss may know that he has told you to investigate the weight of claw hammers; but he has a lot of other matters on his mind, too, and a lot of other people are investigating other things for him. Therefore, before you tell him the weight of claw hammers, tell him that you are about to re-

port on the weight of claw hammers. This principle is illustrated in the report reproduced in Sec. 20.2.1.

(2) An early statement of important results or conclusions. It is now standard practice to state the most important results and conclusions near the beginning of long formal reports (see Chapter 7). Although many people will disagree with us, we believe that short informal reports, too, are usually improved by an early, unsupported statement of the important information being reported. Your boss may have enough confidence in you to take your word on the weight of claw hammers without reading about how you got your data. If he does, you can save him time by giving him the data right away, as soon as you have oriented him. This method is used in the report in Sec. 20.2.1.

(3) A liberal use of heads and subheads. The longer an exposition, the more it needs to be broken up by headings. But a liberal use of headings can often make even a short report clearer and more useful. The memo reports in Secs. 20.2.1 and 20.2.2—which are less than four pages and less than one page long respectively—are both clarified by their subheadings.

6.2 Memo Reports

6.2.1 Use of Memo Reports

A kind of informal report that is useful in a wide variety of situations is known as the memorandum report, or memo report. Although it is often sent to outsiders, the memo report is particularly suitable for the reporting of technical information within the issuing organization. Three kinds of subjects lend themselves particularly to memo reports: trivial subjects, subjects of only temporary interest, and more important subjects that must be taken care of immediately. The preparation of a formal report takes time; you may be called upon to write a preliminary report before you have had a chance to think much about a formal report on the same subject. Progress reports, for example, are often in memo-report form.

A memo report, then, may be used whenever a formal report is not warranted by the length, the importance, or the finality of the subject or by the nature of the audience for which it is written.

6.2.2 Form of Memo Reports

Because of the way they are used, memo reports should be short and to the point. Memo reports as they are now used in companies have become largely standardized both in form and organization. On the other hand, you may modify any standard form to suit your own writing situations within the framework of company requirements.

Memo reports do not customarily have a separate cover or a separate title page. The text begins a few lines under the heading, which appears at the top of the first page. The heading supplies appropriate information from among the following:

Name and address of issuing organization
Report number
Title
Name of person to whom report is addressed
Name of author
Date
Number of pages

6.2.3 Organization of Memo Reports

Each memo report should deal with only one subject. Sometimes, because this kind of report is so short, you may be tempted to string several memoranda together. You will only confuse your reader. Write a new memo for each subject.

The following organization is suggested for the memo report.

(1) *Subject line.* You may find that the title is not enough. Use a subject line containing more information. Put it in all capitals at the beginning of the report proper to draw attention to the content and to make filing easy.

(2) *Statement of the situation or procedure leading to the subject under consideration.* At this point, make clear reference to any link with past work.

(3) *Conclusion, recommendations, or disposal of the problem.* In a sense, this is the meat of the discussion and the part in which the reader is particularly interested. Treat it as fully as need be, but remember that you are writing a memo report.

(4) If necessary, detailed explanation of the thinking or procedure which led to the statement in 3.

Various names are given to these parts. The material in 2 may be called the foreword; 4 may be called discussion. Different orders are often used. For example, if the memo is particularly short, the discussion in 4 may precede the conclusions in 3. In general, the longer the memo, the more useful it is to have the conclusions stated early.

Examples of acceptable memo-report forms appear in Secs. 20.2.1, 20.2.2, and 20.2.3.

6.2.4 Service Reports in Memo Form

You will find the memo form particularly useful when you have to write service reports. Service reports help a company carry on the everyday transmission of technical information. Sometimes they are ends in themselves; for example, a department must write a trouble report when a piece of machinery fails. This trouble report is important in itself; it provides information for the repairman who fixes whatever went wrong. At other times service reports add another dimension; they become the means by which another publication is written, whether it is to be another report or a manual of some kind. An example is the progress report. When you write a progress report, you will not only be telling about something that has happened in the immediate past, but you will probably use the report and others like it when you come to write a final report.

6.2.5 Kinds of Service Reports

Most companies use a great many service reports. They go by various names; some are common to all companies, others are used only by individual companies.

In general, however, report writers write the following service reports at one time or another: the survey report, the progress report, the status report, the trip report, and the trouble report. If you are still in college, you may have occasion to write some of these reports—the first four particularly. We hope that you won't have to write a trouble report.

Sec. 6.1 pointed out the three features regularly associated with all kinds of reports: an early statement of the problem or purpose, an early statement of important results or conclusions, and a liberal use of heads and subheads.

Service reports will incorporate these features, too, but here are some further suggestions to add to those already given.

(1) *Survey Report.*

You may be asked to write a survey report before starting a new project, say a piece of research. If your company is expanding, for example, a survey will be made of new markets, new locations, and other new factors. Or another company may make a proposal and try to sell you something; you may find it necessary to make a survey of certain parts of your company to see if a change is desirable.

The survey report should start with a clear statement of why the survey was undertaken. Then, because the reader will want to see your conclusions and recommendations as soon as possible, these should follow immediately. But surveys are frequently capable of varying interpretations. In a survey report, especially, you should tell what you did, what you saw, what data was available to you. More often than not, you will find it necessary to record oral presentation of statements from other people. Estimated costs and a forecast of future events may be included.

(2) *Progress Report.*

Progress reports are issued at intervals to show what has been done, what is being done, and what is expected to be done. When several people are working on one project, one report often covers the work of all of them.

Progress reports should be made on the basis of a definite amount of work accomplished. They may be made daily, weekly, or at other designated intervals.

A progress report starts out with a statement showing how much ground the report covers, and, unless it is a first report, contains information linking it with former reports. Then may follow a brief statement of the work that had been covered by past reports. This is not needless repetition; it is necessary to show the continuity of work.

Then comes a discussion of the new work being reported. As this is the principal part of the progress report, it should be discussed completely within any limitations of space previously agreed on. Sometimes progress reports contain recommendations for changes in procedure or new courses of action. Just as frequently they do not. They usually end, however, with a prediction of how much will be accomplished in the future, or how much remains to be done.

The *status report* is a special kind of progress report. It may integrate the work of a number of departments or a number of projects, at certain stated times. It will evaluate not only the work being done but also the accomplishments of the personnel involved. For example, in a research laboratory it may not be possible to accomplish anything very tangible or practical over a period of time. Yet it is necessary to know what the research people have been doing. Because the status report usually covers more ground than the progress report, it is likely to be less specific.

(3) *Trip Report.*

Trip reports are usually the record of business trips made and the information gathered. They describe observations and conversations. They contain some of the features of the survey report, but always include a complete list of people seen and digests of conversations and conferences. Because conversations are likely to become repetitious and to digress from the subject, the writer of the trip report must make a special effort to sort out information, to use headings liberally, and to be very careful about where emphasis is placed. Conclusions and recommendations may be included in the trip report, but usually the emphasis is on what actually was covered at the time the trip was made. Places, times, and dates should be accurately set down. A specimen trip report appears in Sec. 20.2.3.

(4) *Trouble Report.*

Even in the best-regulated families, troubles will occur. In college, you will find that laboratory experiments go wrong; you may come up with negative results because of failures of apparatus or failure to follow directions. In industry, defects occur—defects of machinery, performance, and servicing.

The trouble report is usually written for a closed circle of readers.

It states the reason for the report being written in the first place, the situation as it was found by the writer, what was done to correct the situation, and how successful the solution was. There usually follows a clear and careful analysis of the factors leading to the trouble. Often this analysis involves personalities. It is well to state the facts definitely, but impersonally.

The trouble report usually ends with certain recommendations or suggestions. This section may not be found in the beginning, as in many other kinds of reports, because in the trouble report emphasis is on the immediate correction of the trouble. But remember that trouble reports serve the dual purpose of supplying an immediate record and a method of changing and improving existing situations.

6.3 Letters

Technical information is often transmitted in ordinary business letters, especially when multiple copies are not needed. Whenever you write a letter that conveys technical information, you are writing one kind of an informal report. The principles of technical reporting presented in this book apply as well to business letters as to other kinds of reports.

Thus in any business letter you should start out by establishing contact with your reader and orienting him before you plunge into your subject. Although subheads are not customarily used in letters, they are entirely permissible; they can be very helpful, particularly in a long letter or one that treats several subjects (see Sec. 20.2.4).

In a business letter, as in any other report, you should say everything in a straightforward, matter-of-fact way. You should not try to be particularly ingratiating or overfriendly, and neither should you be brusque or in any way rude. It is appropriate, however, for letters to be more personal than other sorts of reports. Business letters do not require any special vocabulary; you should use the same simple, everyday language in them that you use in other reports (see Sec. 13.2).

The form of business letters has become so standardized and is so thoroughly treated in the handbooks that no discussion is needed here. Letters set up in the usual form are reproduced in Secs. 20.2.4, 20.2.5, 20.2.6, and 20.2.7.

We should distinguish, however, between two uses of the business-letter form: (1) for the technical report and (2) for nontechnical information found in the so-called business letter. When you go into the engineering department of a company and letters are mentioned, you will usually find that it is the letter report that is being referred to.

6.3.1 Letter Reports

Like memo reports, letter reports are comparatively short and transmit information as economically as possible. Unlike the usual memo reports, they are as frequently addressed to a person outside the company as to a person within the company.

The letter report may have a form and organization similar to a memo report, but it will carry a formal address and probably other elements usually found in the business letter. In general, the letter report combines the features of the formal business letter and the short informal report. A specimen letter report is reproduced in Sec. 20.2.4.

6.3.2 Business Letters

It is difficult to say where technical information stops and nontechnical information begins. The nontechnical business letter, however, will probably differ from the letter report by being more informal in style, and it will be addressed to a reader outside the issuing company.

Nontechnical business letters can be divided into two types, according to their uses. One type is the *informative* business letter, which provides routine nontechnical information, perhaps in reply to a request. Like any other letter, it should start out by establishing contact with the reader and orienting him before plunging into the subject. (See specimen, Sec. 20.2.6.)

The second kind of business letter is *persuasive*. Suppose you are asking a firm for material to be used in writing a graduation thesis; you may find it necessary first to sell the firm the idea that you need the data, even before you ask for it. Make your request easily understood and easily answerable by using numbers and lists. Break the request into small units, parallel in structure. Any business letter of this kind takes on the form of the sales letter. (See specimen, Sec. 20.2.5.)

In a sales letter, some extra attention must be given to the beginning of the letter to make the reader want to read it. The subject under discussion must then be presented largely from the reader's point of view to appeal to his interest and prejudices, and to get him interested in your problem. The main portion of the letter will be as in any kind of informative writing: a clear exposition of the subject under discussion and a detailed analysis of it. The letter will probably close with a persuasive note in an attempt to get the reader to comply with your request.

A *proposal* letter is in essence a sales letter. In addition to the form just discussed, you might use these devices:

(1) Arrange your material in a sequence conforming to the reader's concept of importance.

(2) Anticipate objections early. Admit them, if you cannot remove them. If they can be overcome, discuss them logically and clearly.

(3) Be more personal than you would be in a letter report, and do not be afraid to develop a relationship with your reader. Look at things from the reader's point of view.

6.4 Job-application Letters

6.4.1 General Principles

A special kind of letter—and an important one—that most people have to write sooner or later is the job-application letter. The application letter can very appropriately be thought of as a combination report and sales letter.

As a report, the letter gives information about you. Again, the principles of good reporting apply: tell your story as accurately, as clearly, as simply as you can, and be as brief as possible without omitting any important information.

On the other hand, the reader may not at first be interested in you. You must persuade him to read your letter, to accept your information, and to do something about you. You are in fact writing a sales letter. You should point up certain individual features about yourself, you should make him want to read your letter by writing in a friendly manner, and you should visualize the kinds of professional and personal qualities the future employer is looking for. You can borrow from what are considered the classic techniques of the sales letter: attract attention, create interest in the product, convince the buyer, and get him to act.

Some people have trouble in beginning an application letter. As in other reports, you should start out by orienting your reader—by telling him what your letter is about. That is, say simply that you are writing to apply for or inquire about a certain job. If you can say honestly that you are writing at the suggestion of some mutual acquaintance, that will serve to establish a personal relationship. (You are not trying to use influence; you are simply employing a perfectly legitimate device to awaken interest.)

Since the letter of application is a report on yourself, you will inevitably have to use the pronoun *I*. Any effort to avoid *I* by means of third-person or passive constructions will sound artificial and stilted (see Sec. 13.13 on impersonality). You may, though, be able to avoid overusing *I* by organizing your material and your sentences very carefully. In an application letter you have to blow your own horn; try to do it in a quiet, objective way that does not sound conceited. If you feel that you are particularly well qualified for the job, tell your prospective employer—it is a valuable piece of information for him.

Another thing any employer would like to know about an employee is that he is enthusiastic about his job. If you can honestly tell your prospective employer that you would particularly like to work at a certain job *in his company*, by all means do so, and tell him why. To make such a statement convincing, you must of course see that no part of your application looks canned or duplicated.

6.4.2 Form of Application Letters

Two general arrangements are in use for application letters: (1) an ordinary business letter that contains all the information being transmitted; (2) a short letter accompanied by a data sheet that contains most of the personal and historical information in tabular form. The data-sheet arrangement is now the more common of the two, but the straight letter has an advantage if you are a proficient writer: it gives you a chance to demonstrate your skill at writing, a quality that most employers value highly. Examples of the two arrangements are given in Secs. 20.2.7 and 20.2.8.

If you do use data sheets, you can reproduce them in three possible ways: (1) you can type them individually; (2) you can duplicate them by Mimeograph or some other process; (3) you can fill in the spaces of a prepared form such as the ones supplied by some colleges. The prepared form must be constructed to fit the needs of many diverse people. For you, it will probably have too much space for some items, not enough for others; it will probably be longer than you need. We believe you will do well to construct your own data sheet rather than use a prepared form. Here, again, you can demonstrate a skill to your prospective employer.

Although many successful applicants have had their data sheets duplicated by one process or another, a duplicated sheet—no matter how neat—gives the impression that you are canvassing the field or circularizing a large number of employers. In order to convey the impression that you are particularly interested in *him,* you should probably send each prospective employer an individually typed data sheet. The effort required to achieve this personal touch is a small matter if it can help you to get a good start in your life work.

Here is a word of advice about the letter and data sheet used in combination. Even though the data sheet will carry the bulk of your information, use the letter to point out interesting features contained in your information and in general to sustain the reader's interest in you.

We have seen letters of application that had no body to them, that contained little more than a reference to the data sheet. The data sheet, being statistical, has no tone or warmth to it, but interest can be aroused in the reader by using the letter to point out any special characteristics you possess, such as knowledge of a second language, an administrative position you held while in college, or a particular job experience you have had.

Most data sheets look alike, especially those from college students. Demonstrate individuality and special talents by means of the accompanying letter of application.

6.4.3 Contents of Application Letters

In general the application letter should contain information about yourself that bears directly on your application—information that will help your prospective employer judge whether you are likely to be well fitted for the job. Below is a list of subjects that are appropriate. You may of course have reason to omit some of them or to add others, and their order is not significant. The starred items are the ones that customarily go on the data sheet if you are using that form; some of the unstarred items may be transferred to the data sheet, too.

Item	Comments
1. Type of work desired and reason.	
2. Date you will be available.	
3. Location desired.	If you are willing to go anywhere, it may be a good idea to say so.
4. Specific reasons for wanting to work for this organization.	Stress this item if you can do it honestly.

*5. Education
    a. Specialization
    b. Record
    c. Honors
    d. Extracurricular activities.
	Usually given with emphasis on professional training. How far back shall you go? Only to a point that bears on this job. Attendance at a certain high school may carry some weight; what kindergarten you went to almost certainly doesn't.
	Opinions differ about the listing of extracurricular activities. At any rate, the purpose of mentioning them is not to show that you were a big man on campus, but to show (1) that you like to mix with people and join in group activities and (2) that you have had experience that will help you in the job you are applying for. Thus you should not go into detail about extracurricular activities unless they have a direct connection with the work you expect to do.

*6. Practical experience.	Usually given in reverse chronological order. The student may appropriately list part-time and summer jobs, to demonstrate his industry and ambition. The older man should probably not go back beyond his professional or related jobs.
*7. Physical condition.	A brief statement that your health is good; or a frank description of any condition *that will handicap you in this job.*

*8. References
    a. Personal or character
    b. Professional.
	Some people say nothing about references in the initial letter of application, but furnish them later if requested. Do not include references in answer to a "blind ad" (a want ad that does not disclose the name of the advertiser).

Item	Comments
*9. Name; address; age; citizenship; marital status.	
*10. A small photograph.	Not required.

Although the ultimate goal of the application letter is a job, its immediate goal is an interview, because most organizations do not employ anybody without a personal interview. Thus almost every letter of application should specifically request an interview. This request often makes an appropriate closing for the letter.

EXERCISES

1. You may be preparing to carry out a project, either for the course in which this book is being used or for some other course. Make a survey of the possible sources of information you will use. Address the report to an instructor and present it in memo form.

2. Write a short progress report on the situation given in Exercise 1. Put it in either memo or letter form.

3. Every so often, and especially if you have started work in your major field, your faculty adviser will want to know what success you are having with your studies, particularly with your major courses. Write such a status report.

4. The field trip is a part of many college courses. Write a trip report addressed to the department in which the field trip originated.

5. Write a letter to a firm or individual requesting information to be used in a term paper or a thesis.

6. Write a letter to a university requesting information about the possibility of your attending graduate school.

7. Write a letter to the president of one of your college activities, suggesting a change of policy in connection with the activity or proposing a new course of action.

8. You need a summer job. Write to a firm requesting such a job. Write two letters: one to accompany a data sheet, the other to contain all the information being transmitted.

7. FORMAL REPORTS

7.1 Form of Formal Reports

Any time you have to extract information from a number of different reports, you will find your task easier if the reports all follow a uniform pattern. And of course it is easier to *write* a report that follows a ready-made plan. Certainly it is a good idea for the reports of any organization all to have the same basic, over-all arrangement of major sections and a uniform system of typography and mechanics. Some organizations, indeed, use the same rigid, standardized outline for all their reports.

But there is a growing tendency to let the outline be general and flexible, so that within the basic framework each report can be constructed to fit its own subject matter, its own purpose, its own audience. *The basic outline suggested in this chapter is thus intended to be completely general and flexible. Furthermore, a number of the items in it are intended to name functions that must be taken care of rather than to be titles for sections of the report.* Within the limits of local conventions, this outline conforms with the prevailing current practice in technical reporting.

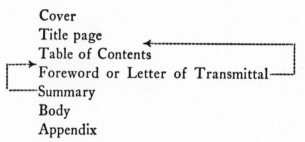

Cover
Title page
Table of Contents
Foreword or Letter of Transmittal
Summary
Body
Appendix

As indicated by the dotted arrows, the summary somtimes precedes the foreword; and if a letter of transmittal is used instead of a foreword, it usually comes right after the title page.

The rest of this chapter discusses the various parts of the formal report. They are taken up not in their order in the report, but in the order in which you will usually work on them. Two short formal reports and portions of a longer one are reproduced in the Appendix (Secs. 20.2.9, 20.2.10, and 20.2.11) to illustrate the discussion.

7.2 Body

7.2.1 Functions; Divisions

What we have chosen to call simply the *body* of the formal report actually performs a number of functions and is usually divided into a number of parts or subsections. It is the longest and most important section of the report; all the other sections are built around it—are auxiliary to it. The body tells your whole story, and it is usually complete and self-sufficient, so that the reader can get the story without reading other sections of the report, with the possible exception of the foreword. (As pointed out in Sec. 7.5, the body may depend on the foreword for some background information, as in the specimen report of Sec. 20.2.9.)

The body does some or all of these things:

(1) It states the purpose of the investigation and provides the reader with enough background information so that he will be able to understand all phases of the report (let us call this function *introduction*).

(2) It tells what you did (*description*).

(3) It tells what you found out (*results*).

(4) It analyzes, interprets, and discusses these results (*discussion*).

(5) It lists *conclusions* and perhaps *recommendations* that follow logically from the discussion (if they are appropriate and if they have been requested).

In some organizations it has been customary to divide the body into separate sections corresponding to these functions. For a report on experimental work, for example, this might produce separate sections called *Introduction, Equipment, Procedure, Results, Discussion of Results,* and *Conclusions and Recommendations.* A slavish adherence to a conventional outline like this often results in (1) a lot of repetition and backtracking and (2) a burial of the most important information under a lot of details, some of which may be routine and of distinctly secondary interest. It is usually preferable to disregard these divisions and to run the parts together in whatever way is natural, logical, and efficient. In most reports other breakdowns will suggest themselves, usually according to divisions of the investigation or of the work being reported.

Remember, then, that the titles of Secs. 7.2.2–7.2.4 name *functions* rather than sections of a report.

7.2.2 Introduction

The need for orienting the reader means that the introduction function must be looked to early; but this does not necessitate a separate section labeled *Introduction* at the beginning of every report. Sometimes the introduction information can be provided once and for all, right at the start, as in the specimen of Sec. 20.2.10. More often this kind of information is needed also at the beginning of each subsection, or perhaps from time to time within subsections. Wherever it goes, the introduction information is highly important. Be sure you take care of it in one place or another.

The part (or parts) of the report that we are for convenience calling *introduction* states the purpose of the investigation and describes the basic scheme of the procedure or methods used. It orients the reader by supplying as much historical background as necessary and then describing the present problem. It may define the scope of the study, discussing limitations or qualifications.

Sometimes a table of definitions of terms or symbols is included in the introduction. The introduction may be a good place to define important specialized terms that are going to be used frequently in the report, but the appendix (see Sec. 7.4) is usually a better place for a table of definitions.

The introduction may describe the organization of the report, so that the reader will know what to expect, or the table of contents (see Sec. 7.6) may provide a sufficient outline.

7.2.3 Description

In order to understand the results of your investigation, your reader must know in general what you did. Certainly you must describe the basic nature of your study or investigation very early in the discussion. But in many technical reports the significant information—the results and the conclusions they lead to—get buried under needlessly detailed descriptions of the methods used. The description of procedures in the body of the report should be no more detailed than is necessary to convey your message.

The basic description of method may sometimes be given once and for all near the beginning of the report, or it may be interspersed among the related parts of the presentation and discussion of results.

Let us say that you have taken care of the basic description, in one way or the other. The full, detailed description may then be treated in four different ways (or combinations of them):

(1) It may be put near the beginning of the report.

(2) It may be interspersed among the related parts of the presentation and discussion of results.

(3) It may be put in the appendix.

(4) It may be omitted from the report entirely, and simply kept on file in the laboratory notebook or company library.

The first two of these alternatives are appropriate when a full description of method is an integral or essential part of the main story—that is, when the primary purpose of the report is to describe a new method or process that has been developed, or when a new or unusual method has been used to obtain quantitative results. Because it describes an investigation that was not routine, the specimen report in Sec. 20.2.10 provides a full description of method before it presents results.

But when the primary purpose of the report is to present the results of an investigation, and the methods used are familiar or routine, then the detailed description is not an integral part of the story, and its presence early in the report simply obscures more important material. Particularly annoying is a prominent list of standard instruments and apparatus.

If the methods and equipment are well known to the readers of the report, it may be sufficient simply to mention them by name and to omit the detailed description from the report. Anyone who wants to repeat the procedure exactly can then get the needed details from the laboratory files. This scheme has been followed in the specimen report in Sec. 20.2.9.

On the other hand, it is often necessary to supply detailed descriptions of even routine procedures for the sake of a minority of readers, or for legal reasons, or for record purposes, or to conform with company rules. You can fulfill these obligations by putting detailed information in the appendix and referring to it at an appropriate point in the text.

In short, it is a good idea to provide only as much information about methods and apparatus as your readers will need.

7.2.4 Results; Discussion; Conclusions and Recommendations

Many reports present results in one section and then discuss them in another. But separate sections for results and discussion are likely to lead to duplication or thumbing back and forth, because it is generally impossible to discuss the results without restating them. The results can usually be presented right along with the discussion of them. This arrangement has been used in the specimen reports in Secs. 20.2.9 and 20.2.1 (the latter happens to be an informal report, but the principle is the same). The specimen report in Sec. 20.2.10 has very little discussion, but what there is has been included in the Results section.

When lengthy tables of numerical results must be included, they can often be put in the appendix (see Sec. 7.4). Then small tables may be excerpted from them, or significant or average values may be taken from them, and incorporated into the discussion. Similarly, the most important curves or graphs may be put into the discussion, while the more routine ones are relegated to the appendix (see Secs. 17.2 and 18.2).

The discussion that goes along with the results explains them and elucidates them. It points out any qualifications or limitations they have, and it brings to light suspected sources of error. It recognizes unexpected results and tries to account for them.

The discussion evaluates the results, and it interprets them and investigates their significance. In this process it probably arrives at conclusions—decisions and judgments based on the evidence presented in the report. If he has been authorized to do so, the report writer may make recommendations in line with his conclusions (see Sec. 2.12).

The conclusions that stem from the discussion should usually be stated in their logical place—at the several points where the discussion has led up to them. They may also be gathered together and restated (perhaps in a section labeled "Conclusions" or "Conclusions and Recommendations") either at the end of the discussion, as in the specimen report of Sec. 20.2.11, or near the beginning of the report, in the summary (see Sec. 7.3).

A discussion seems more complete and is more satisfying to the reader if it comes to a logical and obvious ending on the level of the over-all discussion rather than simply stopping on a note of detail. One kind of ending that is often appropriate is a *summary*, perhaps with emphasis on important results and conclusions. This summary stems from what has gone before; it is an integral part of the discussion, and it may depend on the discussion. It should not be confused with the *independent* summary, discussed in Sec. 7.3, that goes at the beginning of most formal reports.

7.3 Summary or Abstract

Most present-day reports of any length contain a synopsis very near the beginning, either just before or just after the foreword. This synopsis is sometimes called a *summary*, sometimes an *abstract*. Although these two terms are often used interchangeably, some people do make a distinction between them:

(1) An abstract is a more or less *linear* reduction of the whole report.

(2) A summary is a *nonlinear* reduction—a gleaning of the most important points, which may be reproduced full-scale from the body of the report. A summary is likely to be longer than an abstract.

Of these two sorts of synopses, both of which appear in the specimen report of Sec. 20.2.11, the *summary* is usually more useful, and it is likely to be more suitable for formal reports. Therefore most of the discussion that follows will talk specifically about the summary. But in general the principles given apply to every synopsis, whether it is labeled *summary* or *abstract*.

7.3.1 Summary

The initial summary is a synopsis of the body of the report, with emphasis on important findings, conclusions, and recommendations. Therefore it should be written after the main body has been completed. *This summary is not to be confused with the summarizing conclusion that may form a part of the body; it is separate and distinct.*

The purpose of the initial summary is to permit the busy executive (or the busy underling) to get the significant information of the report at once, without having to hunt for it and without having to wade through the whole report. *Therefore the summary must be self-sufficient*—it must be independent of the rest of the report, with two possible exceptions: (1) If the foreword precedes the summary, as it usually does, the summary may depend on the foreword for background information, as in the specimen report of Sec. 20.2.9. Sometimes, though, the summary is put before the foreword, and made completely self-sufficient, as in the specimen report of Sec. 20.2.10. (2) The summary may state unsupported conclusions, the evidence to support them appearing later, in the body.

With these two possible exceptions, then, the summary must supply brief statements of: (1) the nature and purpose of the investigation (unless this information has been supplied in the immediately preceding foreword); (2) the facts or results; and (3) the chief conclusions and recommendations, if any (see Sec. 2.12).

Thus the conclusions and recommendations may be stated in a subsection of the summary, or they may have the status of a separate main section, taking the place of the summary. You will sometimes find statements of fact as well as decisions and judgments under the heading *Conclusions*. When decisions and judgments are included, they are probably the most important part of the report. Furthermore, they are inherently different from facts. Therefore the heading *Conclusions* should usually be reserved for the decisions and judgments, and the facts stated in a separate section of the summary. If this practice is followed, the conclusions and recommendations will form a suggested program of action.

The conclusions and recommendations may be set up as two separate subsections, or they may be put together. Since each recommendation is likely to follow logically from a conclusion or group of conclusions, we believe it is usually better to combine the two.

However the summary is arranged, it should contain only really significant material. It should not contain lengthy quotations of numerical data; if the report is largely numerical, the summary should contain only average figures or the most important figures, which may be arranged in short tables.

Since the body should itself tell a logically complete story, it must be self-sufficient and independent of the summary, too. Thus no information should be contained in the summary that does not also appear in the body.

Because body and summary are independent and each self-sufficient, there is usually repetition from body to summary. In fact, whole sentences from the body are often copied in the summary. Don't let this repetition worry you. Body and summary must each be complete, and many readers will skip one or the other.

Every summary should be as short as it can be without omitting essential information. The length of the summary will vary according to the length of the report and the amount of information in it. Thus no rigid limit can be set; but a summary should seldom exceed two or three pages unless the report is very long.

7.3.2 Abstract

The kind of synopsis that we have been calling an *abstract* appears in many formal reports, and it almost always accompanies the technical paper (see Chapter 10). The abstract often appears entirely separate from its original report or article in one of the journals such as *Chemical Abstracts, Science Abstracts, Biological Abstracts,* and *Horticultural Abstracts* that print nothing but abstracts from other publications. These journals have their own staffs of abstracters; but there is only one way to be sure that their abstract of your report or paper will say what you would like it to say: provide a suitable abstract yourself, along with the original publication. Thus the abstract, perhaps even more than the summary, should be capable of standing on its own feet.

Most abstracts seem to fall into one of two overlapping categories:

(1) the descriptive and (2) the informative. The descriptive abstract describes the report or paper and tells what it is about. It is a sort of prose table of contents. The informative abstract, on the other hand, transmits some of the information—at least the most important points —of the original report or paper. The informative abstract is more valuable than the descriptive, and it is usually to be preferred.

Because the abstract is usually a more or less linear reduction, and because it is usually quite short, the reduction factor is likely to be large, particularly if the report or article is a long one. The greater the reduction factor, the harder it is to avoid the purely descriptive abstract. But you should try to get as much actual information into your abstracts as you can without making them excessively long.

As an illustration of the greater value of the informative abstract, here are two examples each of descriptive and informative abstracts.

Descriptive Abstract	Informative Abstract
A simple method of building close-packed molecular and crystal models is described. It has proved its pedagogic value as well as its many advantages to the research worker. Two diagrams and four photographs are included. The method was evolved in the author's laboratory.	Close-packed molecular and crystal models can be built easily and inexpensively by dipping balls of various materials into latex of 60-percent concentration. Desired colors can be obtained by dipping the balls into a quick-drying water-insoluble paint before the latex is applied. Slight pressure is all that is needed to stick the balls together to form a model. They can be separated by a quick jerk.
Pulse hysteresis loops for a representative group of ferrites are shown and graphs presented for determining the value of pulse permeability to be used in pulse transformer design. The assembly and circuit test of the ferrite-core pulse transformers are discussed and comparisons are made with the present Hypersil-core transformers.	Effective pulse permeabilities of those ferrites range up to a maximum of 450 for 0.1-microsecond pulses, while that observed for 1-mil Hypersil (with air gap) is approximately 100. The assembly and circuit test of 1-to-1 and 3-to-1 ferrite transformers are discussed. The transformers described are equivalent in performance to the Hypersil transformers now used, and yet are more simply constructed and more compact, and can be produced at considerably lower cost. Ferrite-core pulse transformers are admirably suited for 0.1-microsecond pulse applications.

7.4 Appendix

The appendix is a highly useful and important part of the report, even though it is shoved into the background behind the main body. The appendix is the place to put any material that needs to be included in the report but that is not an essential, integral part of the main presentation.

We have stressed the points (1) that every technical communication should be as simple, as short, as unencumbered as it can be and (2) that important ideas should not be buried under a mass of detail. The appendix makes it possible to unload detail information or information of secondary importance from the main presentation, yet still to include it for record purposes or for the sake of those readers who may want it or need it.

Because it plays this role, the appendix is sometimes treated as a dumping ground, and simply thrown together helter-skelter and stuck into the back of the report. It does the reader no good to stumble upon some miscellaneous additional information after he has finished reading the report. He should be given the opportunity of looking up pertinent information while he is reading the related part of the main body. *Thus every section of the appendix should be keyed to the text by a specific reference. Any material that is not connected to the text closely enough to be worth mentioning is not worth putting into the report at all.*

The sections of the appendix should be arranged in some rational order, often the order in which they are referred to in the text, and they should be numbered (or lettered) serially.

The appendix may contain material such as:

(1) Tables, graphs, or illustrations that are an integral part of the main story but that will not conveniently fit into the body of the report.

(2) Tables, graphs, or illustrations that are not used in the main story but that are of interest because they form the basis of it or are related to it.

(3) Tabulations of data that are presented in graphs in the main body.

(4) Detailed descriptions of equipment or procedure, when the body contains only a general or over-all description.

(5) Descriptions of rejected methods.

(6) Samples of forms, data sheets, or questionnaires used in the investigation.

(7) Derivations of equations.

(8) Sample calculations.

(9) Tables of symbols or definitions.

(10) Copies of speeches, contracts, exhibits, or company literature.

(11) Bibliographies.

(12) Any material that must be included for record purposes.

7.5 Foreword or Preface; Letter of Transmittal

The terms *foreword* and *preface,* as applied to reports, are used interchangeably. Since *foreword* is the more common of the two, it will be employed in this discussion.

Most formal reports contain either a foreword or a letter of transmittal, sometimes both. When the letter of transmittal alone is used, it performs the functions of the foreword (Sec. 7.5.1) as well as its own special ones (Sec. 7.5.2).

7.5.1 Foreword

You will notice that the functions listed for the foreword overlap those listed for the introduction phase of the body. The foreword and the body of each report should be planned together, so that they complement each other. There should not be any substantial amount of duplication from one to the other. (Contrast this relationship with that between body and summary: the summary covers the same ground as the body, and may be lifted from it word for word.)

The foreword does some or all of these things:

(1) Provides the reader with general orientation, as contrasted with the complete background information contained in the body. *It tells him broadly what the report is about;* that is, it expands on the title and probably contains a brief statement of basic purpose.

(2) Tells who authorized or requested the investigation to be made or the report to be written (if such information is relevant).

(3) Makes acknowledgments for help received by the author (some organizations use a separate section for acknowledgments).

(4) Makes any pertinent comment about the report.

(5) Refers to other related reports, either those already in existence or future reports that are going to be written about further developments of the same investigation.

7.5.2 Letter of Transmittal

Composition of the letter of transmittal varies widely among those organizations that use this form rather than a foreword. Besides performing the functions listed above for the foreword, the letter of transmittal has the specific job of *transmitting* the report; that is, it says "Here is a copy of the report . . .", or words to that effect.

In addition, the letter of transmittal often refers to specific parts of the report, and it may repeat particularly important points such as conclusions and recommendations. It may also repeat such introductory information as statements of purpose, scope, and limitations. However, the letter of transmittal should not be depended on to transmit any essential information not stated in the report proper, because some readers are likely to skim the letter or to skip it entirely.

When the letter of transmittal contains any appreciable amount of information—that is, when it is in any sense a part of the report—it is usually bound into the report, often immediately after the title page. Sometimes, of course, a report that is complete with a foreword is mailed along with a letter that says simply "We are sending you the report . . .", etc. This kind of a covering letter, too, might be considered a letter of transmittal, but it is usually not bound into the report.

A specimen letter of transmittal is reproduced in Sec. 20.2.12.

7.6 Table of Contents

The table of contents, which should be included in every report of more than three or four pages, does something more important than simply locate page numbers: it provides the reader with an outline, or an over-all plan, of the report. Just as you can do better justice to a banquet if you have been supplied with a menu, so you can read a report more intelligently and more efficiently if you know at the beginning what to expect and where to expect it. The table of contents furnishes the reader with the framework to which he can fit the parts of the report.

Because it performs this important function, it should be constructed carefully.

The table of contents is compiled from the headings in the report. Its entries should be duplicates of these headings, including any number or letter symbols, and they should be arranged in the same outline plan. Thus the contents should clearly indicate the relative weights of the various headings and subheadings, and show their relationships with each other.

No entry should appear in the table of contents that does not also appear as a heading in the text. If it does, the reader may be frustrated and annoyed when he turns from the contents to the text and hunts for a heading that is not there. On the other hand, it is not obligatory to enter every text heading in the contents. Although none of the major headings or subheadings should be omitted, it may sometimes be appropriate to leave out the lightest-weight subheadings, especially if they seem to obscure the main outline; but the headings of any one degree should either be all listed or all omitted.

The table of contents of this book furnishes an example of a table of decimal-system headings. For a table of headings differentiated by typography and indentation, see the specimen report in Sec. 20.2.10.

The table of contents is not to be confused with the *index,* which lists its entries in alphabetical order, and which usually appears at the end of the book rather than the beginning. Only very long or complex reports require indexes.

7.7 Cover; Title Page

The formal report customarily has a binding or cover, usually of cardboard, and a title page, both of which carry identifying information. This information consists logically of several blocks, and it can be clarified by being arranged in physical blocks according to its logical divisions. Furthermore, the more important pieces of information—particularly the title itself—should be emphasized by larger type size or by capitalization. These principles are illustrated in the specimen reports of Secs. 20.2.9, 20.2.10, and 20.2.11.

Secs. 7.7.1 and 7.7.2 list the *minimum* requirements of identifying information for cover and title page, and suggest a few possible additional items. For these pages to do an effective job, they should be as uncluttered as possible, so that the important information will stand out boldly and clearly. Therefore all nonessential items should be removed from the cover and title page and either omitted or put somewhere else in the report.

7.7.1 Cover

The cover should have a label that provides enough information so that the people who have to handle or file the report can identify it without looking inside. Minimum requirements usually are:

(1) Title

(2) Name (and perhaps address) of issuing company or institution

(3) Date of issue

(4) Report number (if any)

In addition, some organizations number the copies of each report serially and put the copy number on the cover.

The covers of students' reports must also carry:

(1) Author's name

(2) Name and number of course or subject

7.7.2 Title Page

The title page repeats all of the items on the cover. It may also carry additional pertinent items such as:

(1) Subtitle or elaboration of main title

(2) Author's name

(3) Name of man or company for whom report was prepared

(4) Further details about issuing agency

(5) Contract or project numbers

(6) Any other necessary information

But remember, do not let the title page get cluttered with unnecessary material.

7.8 Other Elements of the Report

The term "element" is used here to mean any part of the report that has a specific function and therefore needs the writer's particular attention.

It should have been made clear by now that the material being used determines largely the form that the main part of the report will take. The report form should be flexible and not something into which material must be crammed. But the report writer new to the job may not know exactly what to look for. Other elements besides those already discussed should be considered to see if they should be used.

(1) In addition to describing the object, scope, and general purpose of the report, you may need to include a sizeable section on *importance*. Reports are frequently used in connection with technical sales literature; one group of readers may need to know how important you consider the material to be. Some companies, in fact, require that their reports always contain such a section so that the information under discussion can be evaluated and its worth more clearly understood.

(2) When a project cannot be carried out without the help of specially trained people—technicians, specialists, supervisors—you should include in your report a section on *personnel*.

(3) Because a report is written for practical purposes and frequently read by executives who have finances in mind, don't neglect the possibility of including a section on *costs* and *expenditures*. Sometimes recommendations alone do not tell the entire story. If an estimate of costs will have any effect on the over-all report, such a section should be included.

(4) We have stated that the formal report frequently contains a section on background in order to link the present problem with what has been done in the past. Many company reports call for a statement on the future as well, labeled *forecast*. This can be in the undergraduate report, too. It will follow the evaluation of results, conclusions, and recommendations, and will be an extension of them. The forecast is especially needed in the research report; here you can carry your recommendations still further by discussing probable trends and what may be accomplished in the future.

7.9 Outlines of Company Reports

Although form in the formal report should always be subordinated to material, it is a good thing for both student and company writer to know how some companies have designed their reports about their specific products.

The Hercules Technical Reports, a guide to the preparation of reports put out by the Hercules Powder Company, in its preface cites four steps which seem essential in carrying out a competent investigation:

(1) Understand at the outset the objective of the investigation.

(2) Determine the key technical problems to be solved.

(3) Direct the experimental program to solve these problems.

(4) Study the results and draw the correct conclusions from them.

At another place this guide states that "all of your technical reports should have one chief objective—to provide the technical facts and recommendations which must be used by the company management, along with economic and other factors outside the scope of the technical investigation, in deciding on a course of action on the problem you have studied."

The outline given below has been developed as a general pattern for all Hercules technical reports:

> *Introduction*
> What is the *objective* of the work?
> Why is it *important* to the company?
> What is the *background?*
> *Discussion of Results*
> Briefly, what work was done?
> What were the most important results?
> *Conclusions and Recommendations*
> What do the results mean?
> What action do they suggest?
> What future work is planned?
> *Experimental Section*
> How was the work done?
> What results were obtained?
> *Bibliography*
> What pertinent literature was consulted?

Again it must be stressed that the above outline has worked out best for this particular company, as the following has for the Chrysler Corporation:

Sections and Headings	Function
Introductory Section Title Page Preface Table of Contents	Gives background information; lets reader know what the report is about.

Sections and Headings	Function
Summation Section Subject Object Conclusions Recommendations	The heart of the report; gives an over-all view of • what was studied. • what the purpose of the study was. • what you found out. • what you think should be done.
Technical Section Parts or Materials Tested Apparatus Procedure Results Discussion	Give details about • what you tested. • equipment you used. • how you did the work. • what happened. • what was your interpretation of the work.
Graphic-aids Section Tables of Data Curves Drawings Photographs	Gives visual aids in communicating efficiently.
Supplementary Section (Appendix) References List of Symbols Sample Calculations	Presents useful information that is not an integral part of the report.

The outline used by the Oak Ridge National Laboratory is illustrated in the specimen report of Sec. 20.2.11.

EXERCISES

1. It may be that you must write a long formal report for your course in technical reporting. Choosing a suitable subject is sometimes difficult. Write a letter to your instructor telling him of your academic background, your professional ambitions, and any special interests you have. Such a letter will help him to advise you on a subject for your formal report.

2. Your formal report should evolve from as real a situation as possible and should be directed to a real company, group, or individual who can use your information. Set up such a situation.

Assume that a person in authority asks you to supply information that he or his company can use. Write yourself a letter assuming that it is coming from such a person. The letter should explain why you have been asked to do the project and write the report, how much ground you are to cover, what the information is to be used for, and who will be reading the report.

Such a letter will give you proper motivation in writing your formal report.

3. Answer the letter you have received, accepting the assignment, and include a statement of what you are prepared to do.

4. Write a memo report to your instructor. Tell him about the report you have been asked to prepare. Give him as complete an analysis as you can at this time of the material you will be using, the sources of information available, and a tentative outline of the report.

5. Read a report in your field. Write a memo report to your instructor about your reading. Discuss your reading in respect to what has already been said in this book about formal reports. Include with your memo report an informative abstract of what you have read.

6. At several points during the course, write progress reports on your formal report to (a) your instructor and (b) the person or company making the assignment.

8. LABORATORY REPORTS

First let us distinguish between the laboratory *report* and the laboratory *notebook* or *log*. The notebook is a complete record for yourself (or your company) that is filed away and practically never given out for others to read. The report is a vehicle for transmitting to other people the significant information of the notebook. It may be a formal report or an informal report, a letter or a memo.

This chapter is primarily about the college laboratory report. It also contains a brief section on the notebook.

8.1 The Notebook

Your laboratory notebook should be as much as possible like the notebooks used in actual research laboratories. It should contain a running record, or diary, of the work you have done in the laboratory, with entries in chronological order. *This record should be so complete and so clear that it will enable you to duplicate the work after a lapse of years.*

For each project or experiment, the notebook should probably contain these four elements:

(1) A *very brief* statement of the fundamental nature and purpose of the investigation—what it's all about.

75

(2) A clear but succinct record of what you did (and when you did it), including such details as instrument numbers, diagrams of your setups, and calculations.

(3) A record of your results. Numerical data should be supplemented by curves, which may often advantageously be plotted during the conduct of the experimental work.

(4) A *brief* discussion of unusual or particularly noteworthy results or observations.

Unless you are instructed to include them, the laboratory notebook should *not* contain:

(1) Lengthy presentations of theory or textbook material.

(2) Extended discussions of ordinary or routine results.

Like all other forms of technical reports, the laboratory notebook is clarified by a liberal use of headings, sketches, and diagrams.

8.2 The Report

The reports required of students in college laboratory courses may be designed primarily for two different purposes: (1) to serve as a realistic exercise in report writing—to prepare the student for writing the reports that will be demanded of him later, when he is working in industry or in a research laboratory; (2) to serve as a further tool for the teaching of the subject of the course—to drill the student in the details of what he is studying in the classroom.

These two purposes can be combined, and a realistic report-writing exercise can at the same time help to teach the main content of the course. If the assignments for reports are planned with this end in view, the reports will be real technical reports. They will transmit information, and they will have all extraneous material weeded out. They will follow the principles set forth in this book.

Unfortunately, however, the report assignments in many laboratory courses have been laid out primarily as teaching aids, with little thought to their value as report-writing exercises. The resulting reports are likely to be quite unrealistic. The rest of this chapter is addressed primarily to students (and instructors) in those colleges that have not set up realistic reporting procedures in their laboratory courses. If you are one of these students, you will of course write reports that follow the instructions you receive in class. But it is important for you to know how such reports depart from good technical-reporting practice, because all too many engineers and scientists carry over from their college laboratory experience a mistaken idea of what a technical report should be.

(1) The "teaching-aid" laboratory report usually contains a lot of extraneous material, and its elements are in a poor sequence. Here is an outline typical of this kind of report:

    (a) Purpose or object of test
    (b) Discussion of basic theory
    (c) Complete identification of all machines and instruments used
    (d) Detailed description of methods used
    (e) All data in tabulated form
    (f) Results in tabulated form
    (g) Plots
    (h) Conclusions and discussion
    (i) Appendix: computations

A report that follows this outline is largely a transcript of the laboratory notebook. Notice that the most important items—the conclusions and discussion—are badly buried under a lot of detail information. Many of these details might better be omitted from the report entirely, remaining on record in the notebook; or at least they should be relegated to the appendix. In particular, the names and numbers of machines and instruments are seldom significant, and neither is a *detailed* description of method unless the method is new or unconventional. There is seldom any need for a complete tabulation of all the data taken, particularly if they are clearly shown in plots. Usually averages, or final results, are sufficient. And if an outline like this is followed rigidly, as it is in some colleges, it gives the student the erroneous idea that the preparation of a technical report consists of little more than filling in numbers in a ready-made form.

Because it is supposed to drill the student in his classroom work, the teaching-aid report is likely to contain a long discussion of basic theory—usually just a rehash of material that can be found in any textbook on the subject. The real technical report, on the other hand, presents only as much basic theory as its specific audience needs. Because the teaching-aid report is designed to demonstrate to the instructor that the student has read the assignment and done all the required work, it is likely to contain all the information the student can think of on the subject, important or unimportant. Indeed, under these circumstances the student would be foolish to do the pruning job essential to a good technical report.

(2) The audience of the teaching-aid report is an unrealistic one. The author of a real report generally knows more about his subject than his readers do. In fact, he may even have to explain his vocabulary to them. But the student writes the teaching-aid laboratory report to his instructor. Thus the audience probably knows more about the subject —at least in general terms—than the author. The author certainly does not have to furnish general background information or to define terms.

Students can be instructed to make their laboratory reports as much as possible like the reports issued by industrial and research organizations: (1) the laboratory report can follow a flexible outline like the one suggested in Chapter 7; (2) it can be made as brief as possible without omitting essential information; (3) it can be addressed to a specific hypothetical audience—say to the other members of the class, who may be presumed to have the same general training as the writer but to lack his knowledge of the immediate subject. Such a program requires careful planning by the instructors in charge of the laboratory—planning not only of the reporting assignments but perhaps also of the experiments themselves. The effort involved is well worth while. But remember, we are not advising you—the student—to disobey the rules of your own laboratories.

9. THE THESIS

At one time or another you will probably have to write a thesis. Undergraduate courses often require term papers that are theses in capsule form. Many colleges, especially engineering colleges, require a thesis for graduation. If you are working toward an advanced degree, you will certainly find the thesis a major requirement. And many in industry are taking extension courses and advanced degrees requiring theses.

There are strong resemblances between the thesis and the report, and the two are often completely alike. Strictly speaking, a thesis is a document containing information that will advance human knowledge, regardless of when that information will be used. A report, of course, contains highly practical information for more or less immediate use.

Just as the report has become formalized, so has the thesis. But not all thesis forms are alike. Be sure to find out what your college demands. Most colleges publish manuals giving specific directions to fit their individual needs. So, before we go into a discussion of thesis writing, we would like to make these points:

(1) Many of the principles cited in connection with the report apply equally well to the thesis.

(2) All of the things said in Part III on *Tools and Methods* apply to the thesis.

The complete job of writing a thesis will include the following phases: selecting the subject, consulting the adviser, gathering the material, arranging the material, and actually writing the paper itself.

9.1 Selecting the Subject

Selecting the subject takes a lot of time and care. If you are an undergraduate, you may feel that thesis writing is a bothersome chore, devised by teachers as one more task before you graduate. On the other hand, if you are doing postgraduate work, you will by now have the incentive to write a good thesis; and if you are employed, you will have the experience and the insight to see that through the thesis you can make a real contribution.

But you may not be able to select your thesis subject immediately. You will have to reject many ideas before you come upon one that fits the situation. Here are some principles that should guide you:

(1) *The project should require some real research on your part.* Probably the two largest sources of research are experimentation and the study of documents. If you already have a subject in mind, see if it is of such a nature that you can do something in the way of original experimentation in the laboratory. It is doubtful whether a series of laboratory reports will fit your needs. Many laboratory experiments are routine; they have been devised largely as practice work. Your thesis requires that you set up apparatus, use materials, and devise a working procedure that you, not someone else, originated.

These comments apply to library research as well. A paper summarizing the contents of a book is not a thesis; if you find all your material in one or two articles in a reference book, you are performing little genuine research. You must weigh and judge and evaluate your material to see if it fits this first criterion of being a *research* project.

(2) *The research project should be interesting and beneficial to you.* We have indicated that undergraduates sometimes have difficulty selecting good research subjects. They go about the job in the wrong way. A speaker usually makes a poor speech if he discusses a topic that holds little attraction for him. So it is with you as a writer. If you have to plow through your material, fighting boredom all the way, it is doubtful that you will come out with anything very satisfactory.

The subject you pick and the work you do should be useful to you. It should add to your store of knowledge; it should stir your imagination; it should enrich your class work or your professional life.

(3) *The research project should be worth while and of real value.* In addition to looking at your thesis from your own point of view, try to get an objective evaluation. Do you feel that the experiments you perform will fill a gap in the field under consideration? Would there be any point in another person going through the same process? Is it likely that anyone in the future would be inclined to begin another project where you left off?

Especially, is it possible to approach your subject in a scientific manner? Research implies a scientific attitude, open-mindedness, and a readiness to accept changes as they occur. If you start a project with a firm conviction of what you will find, you will probably end up with something that is neither good research nor good writing.

(4) *In selecting a subject, consider the limitations of time, length, cost, and available data.* Pick a subject that can be handled within an allotted time and space. If your thesis (perhaps it is actually a term paper) is required for only one course out of four, you certainly would not be expected to provide as much material as if you were writing for a master's degree. If it is to be completed in one term, don't choose a topic so long that it could be covered only in two terms.

Thesis material is found in many places, and you should carry out an exhaustive search to find it. But there are limitations. Is the data available? Can you, for example, find the material in your college or company library, or must you use outside agencies to help you?

Cost is sometimes a deciding factor. Materials and apparatus may be costly; books may have to be bought and material reproduced. Think of all these contributing factors in choosing a thesis topic.

(5) *Your thesis subject should fit local requirements.* The thesis writer is in a peculiar situation. Not only must he write for the remote reader, he must write under the supervision of an adviser who will determine whether the material is acceptable. And each adviser will have established over a period of time a set of standards by which he will judge the work submitted to him.

(6) *The thesis writer must know where to look for suitable topics.* One source of acceptable undergraduate thesis material is any job

experience you have had, or perhaps a part-time job you are doing. Such practical experience opens up many interesting and profitable topics.

Think of trends in research. Think of the many things still to be done—machines to be invented, processes to be perfected, scientific horizons to be broadened.

Another fruitful source of suggestions is the person who is an authority in a specific field. Your teachers and supervisors can tell you about neglected areas of information. Writers often make provocative statements, or show up contradictions and inconsistencies that should arouse your curiosity. Think of these in terms of possible thesis subjects.

9.2 The Role of the Adviser

Don't look upon your thesis adviser as a person who is to do your work. He is a counselor, not a coauthor. He has a knowledge of what has been done in your field; thus, he saves you time and also introduces you to new ideas. He sees you in relation to other thesis writers; in this way he prevents repetition and duplication. He knows the requirements of your college; he will show you how to arrange your material and how to put it into acceptable form. Above all, your adviser has written a thesis or two himself and can point out the pitfalls.

But treat him as an adviser, not as a proofreader. Listen to what he has to say. When you need information, ask for it only if it cannot be found elsewhere. And, especially, don't expect him to revise your manuscript for you. Nothing will irritate a thesis adviser more than to be mentioned in the acknowledgments as the person who corrected your grammar and punctuation. He should not take the responsibility for a writing job that is yours, and yours alone.

9.3 Gathering Material

The next definite phase is the gathering of material. This is a period when facts and ideas, results and findings, come in from all sides—from books you read, tests you run, the work of other people that you look at.

At the beginning of this phase, look at your problem and try to estimate how big a job it will be. Get oriented to it. Ask yourself some questions. How much laboratory research does the thesis involve?

Often there is the problem of repetition. Should you rerun some of the tests that other people have done, or can you assume that they are definitive and correct?

The question of field trips comes up, too. The conscientious researcher should visit factories and plants to see practical applications of his ideas. You will have to decide how much of this activity is advisable within your limits of time and money.

9.3.1 Interviews

Will interviews be useful to your project; and, if so, how should you handle them? When you are interviewing a busy man, remember that he is granting you the favor. First of all, make the interview easy for both of you by preparing for it. When you get in touch with the person to be interviewed, make it very clear why you must talk with him personally. Prepare a set of questions—not too many, ten or twelve perhaps—and break them up in such a way that they can be answered directly and decisively. Don't trust your memory. Write the answers in a notebook; your man will appreciate having his remarks recorded accurately. And be particularly careful in transcribing statistics and direct quotations.

9.3.2 Questionnaires

You may find it necessary to use a questionnaire as a source of information. Like the interview, the questionnaire must have a reason for being used. You must convince those to whom the questionnaire is directed that you need the material and will be grateful for getting it. Write a covering letter incorporating these two points. The questions should be phrased in the form of a list, not in lengthy paragraphs. There should be comparatively few questions, they should be as brief as possible, and above all they should not be "loaded." A question that practically tells the reader how to answer will be of very little value to you.

Advertising writers put a great deal of effort into the form their questionnaires take. They number the questions, phrase them in parallel form, and provide boxes for positive, negative, and undecided answers. If you feel that you need to know more about the technique of preparing the questionnaire and evaluating it, consult the appropriate books in your library.

9.3.3 Library Surveys

While you are in the library and before you get involved in your project, look over library research possibilities. We have pointed out that your choice of subject may depend on how much help your library can give you. Find out if the library can also help you obtain books from outside sources, such as a state library or special foundation libraries. Find out too if any material you need is restricted or confidential.

You now come to a second step in the gathering of material: a thorough survey of existing literature connected with your subject. The survey will not only be valuable for direct information; you will probably be required to discuss it as a part of your thesis.

Remember that you are building on a base of research and experimentation that has been done by other people before. Your readers will want to know who these people are and what they have accomplished. Track down all available books, articles, reports, and pamphlets. First of all, consult the card catalogues. Then refer to the periodical indexes, bound volumes containing brief synopses of articles published over specified periods. The articles will be cross-referenced like the items in the card catalogue. Two of the better-known periodical indexes are *The Reader's Guide to Periodical Literature* for articles of a general, nontechnical nature, and *The Industrial Arts Index* for scientific and engineering articles. There are also reference indexes on more specific subjects, such as *Chemical Abstracts* and *The Engineering Index*.

These and others will provide information on what has been done before and on material that you may be able to use in a new way. These sources may supply the bulk of your material or may be used to substantiate experimental work you are carrying on.

You will, of course, place your information on note cards as we have suggested in Sec. 3.1.

9.4 Arranging Thesis Material

The main portion of the thesis—the body—resembles the body of a long report. But remember that the motivation for writing it is different, and it is the motivation that will determine the way in which thesis material is arranged.

9.4.1 Introduction

In this section write a statement about the project, defining it, limiting it, and establishing how important and valuable it seems to you. Just as in a report (see Sec. 6.1), write an early statement of important results or conclusions.

9.4.2 Survey of Literature and Recorded Data

This section should mention all the references and documents having any bearing on your specific project. Here the reader will find a comprehensive survey of what has been done by others: what they have written and said, graphic material they have included, and all the statistical detail of past projects.

But you may be asked to do more than mention these records. You may be expected to give an objective interpretation of them. A distinction must be made between bibliography and the survey of literature. The bibliography, placed at the end of your thesis, is a list of the documents that assisted you specifically. The survey, on the other hand, is much larger. It contains not only your specific bibliography but also a record of everything that has been done in the broad field of which your thesis is only a part. Citations must be made by person, date, and place (see Secs. 16.5 and 16.6).

9.4.3 Report on Research

This is the largest part of the thesis. First of all, discuss any special characteristics of the thesis research that have not been treated in the introduction. For example, it may be necessary to mention here that the project was carried out under special temperature conditions or that a new laboratory technique had to be devised.

Then cite any theories, hypotheses, or assumptions. In experimental work, particularly, the reader must know the theoretical basis upon which the entire project rests.

Frequently experimental work requires special laboratory apparatus. If you designed new testing apparatus, this is an important point that must be described and discussed.

After the discussion of theories and materials, describe the procedure you followed, whether your project is library research or experimentation. Follow the best practice of technical description by first giving the over-all view, then taking up each step or phase in more detail.

Because the thesis at least presumably describes an original investigation that explores new territory, it is likely to involve new or unconventional methods. Therefore the description of procedures followed often occupies a more prominent and a larger space in the thesis than it does in the usual technical report, which is more likely to involve standard or familiar procedures (see Sec. 7.2.3).

In experimental work, it may be necessary to run tests of one kind or another. These should be described, and the sequence clearly shown. Then give the results of the tests, putting the data as much as possible in charts, tables, and other graphic forms.

9.4.4 Discussion

Thesis advisers say that the weakest part of many theses is the discussion of results.

Make the discussion as strong and valuable as possible by being objective, although here is the one place in the thesis for presenting opinions and judgments. These must, however, be based on the results of experimentation and research and not on any wishful thinking. Show what your findings mean to the entire area of knowledge, and, if possible, discuss them in terms of the literature you surveyed at the beginning of the thesis.

In the discussion, too, you will evaluate the project as a whole. Don't be afraid to discuss any poor features you feel it has, any disappointments you encountered. State what you think may result from your findings. If you think that any practical applications may evolve, discuss them and suggest methods for extending your work. In that way, you will be helping the next thesis writer.

9.4.5 Summary

The thesis usually ends with a summary. Such a terminal summary will be a gleaning of the most important points taken from the body of the thesis, listed and tabulated for easy reading (see Sec. 7.3).

9.4.6 Other Elements

The typical thesis contains most of these supplementary elements: title page, usually containing a statement of submittal showing for whom the thesis was written; table of contents, often starting out with a thesis statement, which is a one- or two-sentence summary of the thesis subject; preface; abstract; bibliography; footnotes; index; and tables. These elements are discussed in Chapters 7, 16, and 17.

10. TECHNICAL PAPERS AND ARTICLES

The engineer or scientist who has discovered or developed something new is likely to report his work in a paper or article in one of the technical magazines. In general, writing of this kind is governed by the same principles as other forms of technical communication, and almost everything said in this book is applicable.

The term *technical paper* usually describes a piece of writing that is ultimately destined for a journal published by a professional society. Often, it starts out as a manuscript to be presented at a meeting, after which it is printed with little or no revision (but see Sec. 12.2.1 on the reading of speeches).

The term *technical article* is more general. Writing of this kind is usually done directly for a technical magazine put out by a publishing company. Sometimes the readers are not as technically trained as the writer; the article then must become semitechnical in nature. Sometimes the information can be carried to an even wider group of readers in a popularized article.

10.1 Kinds of Periodicals

In this country there are approximately 2000 technical publications. A practicing engineer or scientist can increase his prestige by writing for some of these publications. But the technical writer often writes with another purpose in mind—to keep the reading public aware of what both he and his company are doing. The technical article then becomes part of the public-relations program.

A student, too, may be able to write for technical magazines, for many college writing courses are designed with the very realistic purpose of teaching the student how to write for a real audience. Don't overlook the journals and technical magazines. In addition, you should consider the possibility of writing for your own college publications. There are at least sixty engineering magazines in as many colleges. They offer an excellent opportunity for students to practice technical-article writing.

Technical publications are divided into three general groups:

(1) Journals sponsored by the professional societies. Representative of these are the *SAE Journal* published by the Society of Automotive Engineers; *The Journal of Chemical Education* by the American Chemical Society; and *Civil Engineering* by the American Society of Civil Engineers. Journals of this kind contain papers written by specialists for specialists in the same field.

(2) Technical magazines. Typical ones are *Product Engineering, Machinery, Electronic Design, Machine Design,* and *Factory.* These magazines are more interested in applications of new knowledge than they are in theories, and each magazine attempts to appeal to a distinct group of readers. Because practical matters are stressed by publications of this kind, they require a different kind of treatment than do the journals. Devices, processes, techniques, and applications make up the bulk of the subjects discussed, together with surveys on the broader aspects of technology.

(3) House organs and company magazines. These differ from the other two only in that they originate in industrial companies. *Electrical Communication,* put out by International Telephone and Telegraph, strongly resembles a professional journal. *Westinghouse Engineer* is broader in scope and resembles a technical magazine. Most papers and articles for company magazines come from company employees.

10.2 Preparation for Writing

10.2.1 The Reader

Like other communications, the technical paper and the technical article must be prepared with a definite group of readers in mind. In writing the technical paper, for example, ask yourself these questions: Will your readers be specialists in your own field, with a full knowledge of its problems, its conventions, its language? Or will they be predominantly technically trained people with other specialties, who are conversant with the fundamentals of science but need instruction in some of the elements of your particular field? In general, the readers of technical *papers* are more interested in basic principles and in new ideas and experiments than they are in practical applications.

The readers of technical *articles* usually want to know what is going on in the technological world. They are first of all interested in facts, rather than in theories. They will also want to know how to apply such information. They will expect the writer to stress the usefulness of whatever is described, be it a device, machine, or process, and especially to show its practical application to their needs.

10.2.2 The Material

The material for technical journals is as broad as human knowledge and at the same time as specialized as the scientists who write it. Laboratory experiments, theses of all kinds, learned speeches delivered at professional meetings—from these come the many and diversified topics adapted by the journals.

Technical magazines, on the other hand, will be more restrictive in the material they accept. Each magazine has its own needs, its own requirements, and its own concept of what its readers want. Consequently, ask yourself the question: what kinds of topics seem to create the greatest interest in editor and reader?

Among subject classifications appearing in the technical magazines, these head the list:

Machines and devices	Safety
Processes and procedures	Increased efficiency
Plant descriptions	Costs
Operation and performance	Personnel problems
Maintenance	Technological trends

10.3 Writing the Article

10.3.1 The Technical Paper

The construction of a technical paper is essentially the same as the construction of a report, but the paper usually consists simply of one main presentation, in logical order, plus a short abstract. (See Sec. 7.3.2 for suggestions about the abstract.) Although the technical paper does not contain all the separate elements of the formal report, it can practically always benefit by being broken up into logical sections with headings and subheadings (usually of not more than two degrees).

Many technical papers seem to follow this outline:

(1) Abstract.

(2) Purpose, explaining, as in the report, what the author is doing, and why, and in general orienting the reader to the topic under discussion.

(3) Conclusions. Again, as in the report, the reader is entitled to get his principal information at once.

(4) Procedure, telling how the project was carried on, with all the detailed steps coming after the broad, over-all view.

Another outline that is finding increasing favor is:

(1) Abstract

(2) Introduction

(3) Results

(4) Discussion

(5) Experimental (set in smaller type when printed)

(6) Conclusions or Summary

In writing for professional journals, contributors should refer to any style manual provided by the journal, such as those listed in Sec. 20.3. Most libraries should have them. Here is the required outline for articles found in the style manual of The American Society of Mechanical Engineers:

(1) Title

(2) Author's name, business connection, and mailing address

(3) Abstract

(4) Body of paper

(5) Appendixes

(6) Acknowledgments

(7) Bibliography

(8) Tables

(9) Captions for all illustrations

(10) Photographs and other illustrations

10.3.2 The Technical Article

The technical article, slanted for a more commercial and business readership, is likely to follow this outline:

(1) Lead

(2) Lead-in

(3) Body

(4) Ending

We will consider each one of these parts in turn.

(1) *Lead.*

The lead is usually one paragraph in length; it is the first thing read; and it has the dual function of introducing the reader to the subject in a general way and of attracting attention. The kinds of leads given here are those most frequently used.

The offer of something new:

> Aluminum is used instead of copper for electrical conductors because it offers opportunity for reducing cost and weight. . . .

Summary:

> Broadly speaking, dimension control has two main uses in design and in manufacture. . . .

Historical:

> Graphical symbols are one of the oldest forms of written language known to man. The ancient caveman drew crude pictures of things about him. . . .

Comparison of old and new:

> Although the potentialities of computers were recognized early in the nineteenth century, large-scale digital computers are a recent development. . . .

Reference to authority:

> Charles F. Kettering, consultant to the research staff and a director of General Motors, believes that men can be taught to invent. . . .

(2) *Lead-in.*

The lead-in is the stepping stone by which the reader gets to the main portion of the article. Some authorities call the lead the point of *general interest* that attracts attention and the lead-in the point of *specific interest* that holds attention. The lead-in tells you specifically what the rest of the article is to be about. In most technical articles, which are read almost solely for their informational value, the lead and the lead-in overlap and may be contained in a single statement. The lead-in statements given here are typical. Imagine that a lead sentence or paragraph precedes each.

Statement of specific use or idea:

> One of the neatest and fastest-growing approaches to the solution of some of these problems [efficient heat transfer and corrosion prevention] is the use of volatile, film-forming amines. . . .

Summary:

> We can best determine the true importance of the engineering staff by reviewing its objectives, its relationship to the rest of the company, and its contributions. . . .

Explanation of purpose:

> This article presents, as comments from both members of a typical team of engineer and technical writer, the most frequently voiced of these principles. . . .

Here are some examples of the lead and lead-in combination.

Lead (reference to authority)	A significant provision of the patent statute is: "Subject to the provisions of this title, patents shall have the attributes of personal property. Applications for patents or any interest therein shall be assignable in law by an instrument in writing."
Lead-in (statement of specific idea)	On this provision rests not only the right of an inventor to sell or transfer his patent, but the collateral right to license its use to others while retaining ownership of the patent and its attendant monopoly.
Lead (summary)	To promote participation in technical society work, the governing board should create an encouraging climate and an atmosphere of enthusiasm, promote individual activity among its members, assist engineers, and publish information of specific interest.
Lead-in (purpose for writing)	We have repeated these basic principles for one purpose—to call attention to the apathy that exists among the membership of some societies.

Lead (something new)   Scientists at R.P.I. now have a new instrument at their
                                command, an electron microscope, which will enable them
                                to examine particles too small to be seen with the most
                                powerful optical microscopes.

Lead-in (statement of   We know that the answers concerning the structure and
specific use)   function of materials, both living and nonliving, can best
                                be found by observing details many times too small to be
                                seen with conventional optical systems. Although it may
                                have other functions, the new electron microscope will be
                                used to extend research into the field of organisms.

(3) *Body.*

The body of the technical article must be based on solid organization.
All of the devices and techniques already discussed apply to this main
portion. Be sure that you plan ahead and make an outline. Magazine
editors can see through a poorly organized piece of writing.

If you take the time to look over material already published, you will
find that three methods of organizing the body of the article are at the
top of the list.

(a) *Chronological.* As discussed in Sec. 2.7, the chronological
method presents material as it occurred in time. First things are discussed first. This method is particularly adaptable to the description of
processes.

(b) *Importance.* This second plan is based on the assumption that
certain parts of a machine or steps in a process are more important than
others. Because the interest of the reader may wane as he reads the
article, it may be wise to discuss the most important elements toward the
beginning of the body.

(c) *Climactic.* Some subjects, especially those of a persuasive or
argumentative nature, lend themselves to a treatment that proceeds from
climax to climax. In this procedure, you may make a point, then go on
to establish others through logical arrangement. The article thus contains a series of high points that establish certain principles.

To outline the body of your article is not enough. You must always
imagine the reader at the other end and learn how to hold his attention
at the same time as you give information. Most technical articles are
supplemented by illustrations and other graphic material. Do not neglect, however, other methods of bringing your ideas to life and making
your statements authoritative. These devices are commonly used:

Statistics. Statistics give authority and proof to our words. But don't use statistics entirely by themselves, in the form of figures and tables only. Put them in situations involving people and places.

References from the experts. Interpret your information in terms of people of ability and reputation. We must recognize, however, that reference of this kind is not necessarily proof. It is simply another way of lending weight to your ideas.

Incidents. Readers can better visualize an abstract piece of information when it is put in terms of description and narrative. An incident is something happening; describe it in terms of what happened in the laboratory, who worked on the project, unusual occurrences, and the place and time involved.

Comparisons and analogies. When the material is unfamiliar to the reader, translate it into terms of things he already knows.

(4) *Ending.*

Many writers find it difficult to end their articles (see Sec. 2.7.3). Think of the ending as making a full circle with the beginning. For example, if it was necessary to begin the article with a summary, it may be as necessary to end with a summary. These are some of the endings most commonly used:

Summary
Logical conclusion
Application of basic ideas
Forecast of future events

10.3.3 The Semitechnical Article

You may find yourself writing for a more general audience than those who read professional journals and technical magazines. Magazines such as *Popular Science* and *Science Digest* come to mind. And some of the company magazines, because they advertise their companies as well as give information, tend to favor more popularized articles.

The basic techniques for semitechnical articles are those used in technical articles. But the following devices should help to make your material clearer to the untrained reader.

(1) Consider using other leads than those already cited. The more popularized the article, the more these leads will be used:

Striking statement or question
Description of people and places
Beginnings that tell a story
Tie-in with current events
Dialogue and other human-interest features

(2) Write very short sentences and paragraphs.

(3) Use short words with action and visual appeal; avoid technical terms.

(4) Provide headings.

(5) Write to the eye as well as to the ear. Use listings, tabulations, underlining (or italic type), capitalization.

(6) Quickly identify things by their shape, size, color, material, texture.

(7) Make statements in a positive manner.

(8) Use repetition to emphasize points.

(9) Personalize your writing. The farther you move from pure reporting, the more effective it is to put yourself and other people into your writing.

(10) Don't try to be unique in your methods of presentation. As in other forms of reporting, the semitechnical article gives information.

Because your library has many examples of technical papers and articles, none has been reprinted in this book. Look them up in the journals and magazines, and inspect them critically. Here is a list of typical articles for you to consult:

Almen, J. O. "Fatigue of Metals," *Automotive and Aviation Industries* (Feb. 1 and Feb. 15, 1943).

Bradley, Robert R., and Dohovan, John G. "Chemical Rocket Engines," *Sperry Engineering Review* (Sept.-Oct. 1957).

Chadwick, Joseph H. "The Anti-Roll Stabilization of Ships," *Sperry Engineering Review* (Nov.-Dec. 1956).

Chinard, Francis P. "The Definition of Osmotic Pressure," *Journal of Chemical Education* (Feb. 1954).

Depp, W. A., and Meacham, L. A. "Station Apparatus, Power and Special Systems," *Bell Laboratories Record* (June 1958).

Eibling, J. A., and Landy, B. A. "The Steam-Generating Station as a Source and Sink for the Heat Pump," *Mechanical Engineering* (July 1951).

Forrester, Jay W. "Digital Information Storage in Three Dimensions Using Magnetic Cores," *Journal of Applied Physics* (Jan. 1951).

Gaber, David. "Forecast for Sulfur," *Stanford Research Institute Journal* (fourth quarter 1957).

Goubau, Georg. "Single-Conductor Surface-Wave Transmission Lines," *Proceedings of the I.R.E.* (June 1951).

Gray, Albert Woodruff. "Patent Licensing," *Machine Design* (Apr. 5, 1956).

Gray, George W. "The Ultracentrifuge," *Scientific American* (June 1951).

Hix, C. F., and Purdy, D. L. "Creativity Can Be Developed," *General Electric Review* (May 1955).

Jacobs, H. L. "Waste Treatment Methods—Recovery and Disposal," *Chemical Engineering* (Apr. 1955).

Macurdy, Lloyd B. "Standards of Mass," *Physics Today* (Apr. 1951). Also in National Bureau of Standards, *Technical News Bulletin* (Jan. 1951).

National Bureau of Standards. "Electronic Counting of Paper Money," *Technical News Bulletin* (Apr. 1951).

Pierce, John R. "Space-Charge Waves," *Physics Today* (Feb. 1949).

Sanders, Herbert L., and Yeager, John A. "Synthetic Detergents for Domestic Dishwashing Machines," *Industrial and Engineering Chemistry* (Apr. 1951).

Sonneborn, T. M. "Partner of the Genes," *Scientific American* (Nov. 1950).

Strong, John. "Experimental Infrared Spectroscopy," *Physics Today* (Apr. 1951).

Struve, Otto. "The Evolution of the Stars," *Scientific American* (Mar. 1953).

Svirsky, Leon. "The Atomic Energy Commission," *Scientific American* (July 1949).

Walker, A. C. "Growing Quartz Crystals for Military Needs," *Electronics* (Apr. 1951).

Westman, H. P. "Graphical Symbols for Electrical Diagrams," *Electrical Communication* (Dec. 1954).

Yates, L. D., Roy, L. F., and Meline, R. S. "Improved Fertilizer Plant Design," *Chemical Engineering* (June 1951).

EXERCISES

1. Select a paper from each of three successive issues of a technical journal. Analyze these papers in order to determine the requirements of the journal for form and presentation. In report form, record your survey and analysis.

2. Make a similar analysis of three articles from a technical magazine. In addition, come to some conclusions about the differences between writing for journals and writing for magazines.

3. Select a technical paper and write an informative abstract of it.

4. For a projected article for your college magazine, write a short report analyzing your own fund of knowledge, the interests of your likely readers, and the methods by which you will present your material.

5. For purposes of practice only, select a technical or scientific subject and write the beginning of an article as it might appear in a journal, a technical magazine, and a general magazine.

6. Select a technical magazine. Prepare a short article for publication describing a new product, a new procedure, or a significant trend in technology.

7. Prepare an outline for a technical paper or article. Justify your outline by referring to the material with which you will be dealing.

8. Prepare a short research paper to be submitted to a professional journal. Base the paper largely on library work and documentation.

9. Before you start writing the rough draft of a technical article, state the devices you will use to lend weight and authority to the body of the article. Submit your statements in numbered and listed form.

11. INSTRUCTIONAL WRITING

11.1 Style and Form

Frequently instructional writing is combined with report writing. In style and form, instructions range from the formal, terse set of commands so often found in business memoranda or posted in college laboratories to the informal how-to-do-it article printed in popular magazines.

In structure, instructions can be as simple and direct as "Turn out the lights," and as complex as the multipage manual on the maintenance of an airplane.

In any case, the first principle is to present the individual points as briefly as possible, and to make them clear and capable of easy reading. After all, you cannot afford to wade through an essay on fire prevention if the house is on fire.

A second principle is to write in such a way that the instructions are authoritative and the reader is easily persuaded to carry them out. Most people prefer to know why they are being asked to do things, and when they know they are usually convinced.

Instructional writing profits by most of the devices listed in Chapters 2 and 4. You may have to define your terms before you can issue orders.

If a machine is involved, it is usually necessary to describe it and explain how it works. Processes, too, are frequently involved in instructional writing; study the techniques for explaining processes (see Sec. 4.2) and apply them to this kind of writing. In particular, remember the advice of Sec. 2.4 to deal with the whole before getting down to any of the parts.

11.2 Formal Instructions

Any instructions should be well planned in advance and put in a step-by-step arrangement. You will only confuse the reader and make the result unpredictable if you neglect to mention an important step at the right time.

The language should be simple and suited for the particular people who will be carrying out the project. It may be necessary at times not only to give positive instructions, but to include explanations and precautions. Explanations will satisfy the reader's desire to know why he is doing a particular thing; precautions will save him from errors in judgment and sometimes from bodily harm.

Formal instructions form the basis of industrial manuals and instruction books. Therefore, the elements suggested here will be useful to the student and to the industrial writer alike. A specimen of formal instructions is reproduced in Sec. 20.2.13.

11.2.1 Title

The title should be short and positive, and explain what the instructions are intended for.

11.2.2 Purpose and Scope

It is advisable to include a short introductory paragraph, explaining the purpose of the instructions, how much ground they cover, and what the result should be.

11.2.3 Equipment and Materials

It may sometimes be necessary to follow the introductory portion with a section of general information especially concerned with equipment and materials, particularly if these must be devised especially for the project.

11.2.4 Specific Instructions

Especially in simple problems, and at the same time for more technical material, specific instructions should be stated in the imperative mood—command language. For example, in giving instructions for making a sundial, do not say, "You should cut the design in two along the 12-o'clock line." Instead, say, "Cut the design along. . . ."

11.2.5 Explanations and Precautions

Explanations of apparatus and materials to be used in carrying out the instructions are usually placed in the indicative mood, the language of discussion as distinguished from the language of command. For example, at the end of his instructions about making the sundial, when he felt the need for further explanation, the writer changed from imperative language to say, "Through the year the sun and our clocks do not exactly agree. Sometimes the sun is 10 to 15 minutes ahead, sometimes behind."

On the other hand, if a precaution is of vital importance, don't hesitate to put it in the imperative mood—and underline it and type it in capitals, if necessary.

11.2.6 Numbering

Formal instructions are usually numbered, with each step placed in a separate paragraph.

11.2.7 Other Devices

Instructions within a specific section may be capitalized, underlined, or otherwise set off to distinguish them from the explanations and precautions. The latter, for example, are often indented beyond the usual margin, or put in separate paragraphs, or placed in parentheses. If not so important, they can be held over until the end.

Some formal instructions require check points. These sectional headings indicate where the reader is to check on what he has been doing up to a particular point. A drawing or some means of visual representation can help the reader decide whether he is on the right track.

11.2.8 Visual Presentation

Instructions are often clarified when accompanied by illustrations, charts, and other graphic material (see Chapter 18).

11.3 Informal Instructions

The wider the reading public to whom instructions are addressed and the less compulsion put on the reader to follow them, the more you will resort to the techniques suggested in Chapter 10 for the technical article. You may have to use a vocabulary containing a minimum of technical terms and many words of high imaginative content. Often the first paragraph, with its general introduction to the subject, must be slanted to attract attention and convince the reader of the value of the project. All the devices of adaptation and popularization—analogies, examples, incidents—should be employed.

But when actual instructions are given, the formal method is customarily used.

11.4 The Simple Manual

Suppose that you were asked to write a simple manual. How would you go about it?

First of all, analyze your problem and decide to what extent your reader must be instructed. If a page will do, don't try to be fancy and write a half dozen pages of elaborate directions.

Start writing the manual only after you have made a careful study of the process involved. For example, if you are writing instructions for a machine, operate it yourself, talk to others who have operated it, and in general profit by these experiences—both the successes and the mistakes —before you make up the format of your manual.

Gain as much information as you can from all sources. Investigate the experiences of others. See if a set of instructions already exists. Even if it is not satisfactory, it may give you a framework on which to hang a new edition. And don't neglect interviews, questionnaires, and other personal sources.

How-to-do-it writing (and manual writing falls into this category) benefits tremendously from graphic material. The quantity depends, of course, on how complicated are your instructions, how large a distribution you will have, how much money you can spend. But certainly drawings of machines, and pictures of people and devices in action, will help the reader to carry out the instructions. You must decide which parts of your write-up will be helped by illustrations and where you can obtain them. For a more detailed discussion of graphic material refer to Chapter 18.

As soon as possible make a rough outline of the manual as a whole. Decide on the approximate number of pages you will have; this will be determined by the complexity of the device, the time available, and costs. Investigate the various kinds of reproduction available; see Sec. 16.11.

Before writing the manual, experiment with a few tentative layouts and format designs. Decide whether to use the entire page width, or double, or even triple, columns. Decide on illustrations, and indicate where they will be placed. As in reports, headings are almost mandatory; show where they will appear. They may be only tentative, but they will show you how to arrange your material.

The next step involves preparation for writing, although you will probably have done some writing already. And here a clear outline can save you a lot of work. At the same time, adjustments are constantly made between the outline and the manuscript right up to the final draft.

Remember, too, that the three kinds of expository writing are usually found in a manual: *informative,* which is the basis of so much report writing; *instructional,* which we have been discussing; and *persuasive,* as used in articles and sales literature.

The first part of a manual, then, will probably be a combination of informative and persuasive writing. It will be an introduction orienting the reader to the purpose and function of the manual and the procedure with which it is dealing. The style of the introduction will depend on the knowledge the reader already possesses and how necessary the manual will be to him.

This section may be followed by one dealing with materials and equipment or descriptions of other items necessary to carrying out the instructions. Devices already recommended in this book should be examined— lists, tabulations, and so on.

The next step involves the detailed instructions. Pay particular care to their arrangement, and determine whether the techniques of formal instructions, or those of a more informal approach, should be followed.

In the actual writing, use the general principles already recommended. Use the imperative mood as much as possible. Assume that the reader knows little about the project itself; therefore be simple, and include analogies and comparisons. Make a careful check of your details to be sure they are accurate. Many procedures do not succeed because the directions are incomplete and inaccurate.

The final step in the preparation of the manual will be one of check-ing. Ask someone to go through the procedure as you have roughed it out. Only when all its parts are clearly written should you consider the manual ready to be reproduced in its final form.

EXERCISES

1. Prepare a set of instructions to be used in one of these situations or in a situation of similar importance:

    (a) In case of fire
    (b) Sharpening a lawnmower
    (c) Changing a tire
    (d) Replacing parts in a radio or television receiver
    (e) Operating a simple electric saw

2. Prepare a set of instructions to be used in operating a simple piece of apparatus found in a laboratory. The instructions are to be handed out to students performing a laboratory experiment.

3. Prepare a set of instructions for operating a simple machine or device used in the home.

4. In instructional form, write a description of a job which you held during the summer or which you are now holding.

5. Write a report to your instructor analyzing an instructional manual used with a machine or a process. It may be for operations, mainte-nance, or repair. Show the characteristics of the manual, especially in relation to the principles discussed in this chapter.

6. Select a manual used in connection with a simple operation. If you think that the manual is not clear, reorganize the material. By

headings, show the various units, indicating what should be placed under each heading.

7. Gather data to be used in the preparation of a simple manual. Put the data in workable form and give it to another student to organize as in Exercise 5.

8. Write a short but complete instructional manual for a practical purpose. Some suggested uses are: for the steward in your fraternity; for a student registering at your college; for building a simple device; for operating a machine in a laboratory.

12. ORAL REPORTS AND SPEAKING IN PUBLIC

Every time you discuss your work with your boss or one of your colleagues, you are making an oral report. Most engineers and scientists do this sort of informal technical reporting very well. But when you write a paper for one of the journals, you will probably first have to deliver it orally at a meeting of a professional society. This more formal sort of oral reporting calls for greater skill and more planning than everyday informal conversations about technical matters. The better known you become in your profession, the more likely you are to be called on to give other kinds of talks and speeches. In addition to the oral report before a professional society, you may find yourself speaking at business conferences, taking part in panel discussions, and giving nontechnical speeches in your community. In this chapter, which is far from being a complete treatise on public speaking, you will find some pointers that should help you to do an effective job whenever you have to talk before a group of people.

12.1 Material for the Speech

12.1.1 Technical Speeches

If you have attended meetings of the professional societies, you have probably discovered that all too many of their speakers simply stand up and read the papers that they have written for publication in the journals. Now this is poor practice for a number of reasons. Most people can absorb knowledge more readily through their eyes than through their ears: when they read a paper they can assimilate far more complicated ideas than they can when they listen to a speech. Therefore an oral report must in general be *simpler* than its written counterpart.

Furthermore, the listener cannot turn back and reread the passages that he has missed or that he has forgotten, and he cannot pause to mull over particularly difficult ideas. Therefore the oral report must not only be simple; it must supply frequent reminders and restatements of key points. Consequently, it must contain considerably less information than a written report of the same length.

Finally, written language and spoken language are quite different. As a result, the words that look natural and appropriate on paper sound unnatural and inappropriate to the ear. Spoken language is, naturally, easier to listen to than written language.

For all of these reasons, the written paper is very seldom suitable for oral presentation. Any time you have occasion to deliver a formal talk, by all means take the time and the trouble to prepare a version of your material that fits the needs of listeners, not readers.

Some societies ask their speakers to give 10- or 15-minute oral presentations of papers that might take 30 minutes or more to read through. If you condense a 30-minute paper to a 10-minute talk by linear reduction—that is, if you omit none of the ideas but only some of the explanations—you will present your hearers with a concentrated dose that they will be unable to understand even if they want to. Any time you have to prepare a short oral version of a longer paper, pick out the two or three most important points of the paper, and develop them thoroughly and leisurely. Refer your listeners to the printed paper for the minor points if you want to; but otherwise, exclude these matters rigorously from your talk.

12.1.2 General Speeches

Other types of speeches utilize the same principles. However, you will have to think of some other devices as well. For example, one of the first things you should do is to estimate what kind of audience you will have; find out as much about it as you can before you even pick your subject. Audiences can be divided into a number of groups based on age, education, social background, interests, and prejudices. You may use the same topic for any one of these groups, but if you have once given the speech before a club group you will probably find it necessary to make some important changes before delivering it to a high school audience.

Time and place will sometimes cause you to modify your speech. In general, people are more eager to learn when they are brought together during daytime hours; evening talks are more likely to be on the lighter or more inspirational side. A church pulpit is not the best place from which to deliver a humorous speech, as some humorists have discovered to their chagrin. People are conditioned not to laugh in church. Certain occasions seem to call for distinct types of speeches. For instance, audiences expect to be inspired and uplifted by Memorial Day talks and commencement addresses.

A cardinal principle of general speechmaking is to choose a subject that interests you and about which you know a great deal. If you are giving an oral report, this is what you will be doing anyway. But sometimes groups will try to impose a topic upon you. If it doesn't fit you, don't tackle it. If you are given free rein, choose a topic so close to you that your enthusiasm will be transmitted to your audience. There is no better way of preventing or overcoming stage fright than knowing your subject and having a tremendous interest in it. Such a combination makes you an expert; you can feel superior to your audience. And a feeling of superiority usually dissipates any nervousness you might otherwise have.

Many speeches get off to a bad start because the speaker hasn't sufficiently thought out his opening remarks. Provide a good opening for your talk by devising something that will attract attention and carry you into your specific subject. Naturally, this beginning must be compatible with your material and the audience you are addressing.

If you are giving out straight information to a class or a conference, do not cheapen your talk with a sensational beginning. On the other hand, if you are persuading the audience to accept a new idea or follow a new course of action, you may have to start with something novel or different. Stories, quotations, ironic or contradictory statements, references to well-known people—these are some of the devices that you can use.

Every speech should have a center around which everything is arranged. Ruthlessly cut out anything that does not clarify or illuminate your central ideas. Some speakers prepare too much material; they include anecdotes and stories interesting to themselves, but with little bearing on the speech as a whole. Such a speech may interest an audience momentarily, but in the long run it will only be confusing.

If your speech has a strong core, it will be much easier to put the individual points together. They may be arranged chronologically or according to importance, or built up to a series of climaxes. And the material will shape up all the better if you discard anything that doesn't really belong.

The heart of any speech is the examples used in it. It is not enough to tell your audience what the main points are. You must bring them alive. Think how effective visual aids—slides and movies—are. Since you can't provide slides and movies for every speech, do the next best thing: supply pictures and examples for the mind's eye. Every time you introduce a main topic or attempt to drive home an idea, see if you have provided a good down-to-earth example. Make it vivid and colorful. Use familiar words, action words, picture words.

The ending of a speech should be sharp and decisive. For most speeches, it is essential that you demand something of the audience, anything from merely asking it to think about a proposition to a much more positive demand like contributing money to a worthy cause. So, in addition to making the ending decisive, try to bring some action into it. If you have been giving information, it may be necessary to summarize what you have said. If you have been arguing some cause, come to a conclusion; if you have been talking in a light vein, end with a story.

12.2 Delivery of the Speech

12.2.1 Type of Delivery

The prepared speech (as opposed to the impromptu or spur-of-the-moment talk) can be delivered in three ways: (1) it can be read; (2) it can be memorized and recited; or (3) it can be presented extemporaneously, with or without notes. The third of these methods is usually by far the best.

The speech that is read seldom sounds fresh or vigorous; it is usually dry and humdrum. The reader's voice settles into a monotonous drone, and the listeners settle low into their seats. The reader must spend most of his time looking at his manuscript rather than at his listeners, so that he loses touch with them. As a result, he cannot tell when he needs to slow down or to provide further explanation of a point that is baffling them, or when he is boring them by dwelling too long on a point that does not interest them. The people who can read aloud in a way that is lively and stimulating are few and far between. Unless you are one of them, you will do better not to read your speeches except when you are required to. After all, what does one get from hearing a speech poorly read that cannot be gotten better by reading the paper oneself?

Very few people can sound natural or convincing when they are reciting a memorized speech. Most people have to concentrate so hard on calling up the memorized words that they lose sight of the meaning of what they are saying. Consequently their delivery is expressionless, singsong, and probably too fast. But even worse, when the reciter of a memorized speech once gets off the track, he is lost. Logic or knowledge of his subject won't tell him what to say next; only the resumption of a complicated and delicate mental pattern will get him started again, and over this process he has no control. *Don't* memorize a speech.

The extemporaneous speaker, on the other hand, has almost every advantage over the reader or the reciter. Because he is thinking what he is saying, he can speak with expression, emphasizing the important ideas. He looks at his listeners, gauges their reactions to what he is saying, and adjusts his speed and his approach accordingly. But don't get the idea that the extemporaneous speech can be dashed off with no planning or preparation beforehand. The preparation for a good extemporaneous speech requires at least as much work as the writing of a paper of the same length.

The rest of this chapter gives some pointers on the *manner* of presentation. They are aimed specifically at the extemporaneous speaker. Most of them will be helpful also to the reader (if you must be one). The reciter we will not consider at all, because we trust we have persuaded you never to memorize a speech.

12.2.2 Manner of Delivery

Some speakers have such good memories and so much confidence in themselves that they can give long and complicated talks smoothly without referring to notes. Most people, though, do better—or at least *feel* better—if they have some notes to bolster their memories. While no audience objects to a speaker's using notes, they should be as unobtrusive as possible. Don't put them on the 8½ x 11-inch paper you use for most purposes, but on 3 x 5-inch cards that will fit almost unnoticeably into the palm of your hand. Make the notes just as brief as possible. Usually a bare topical outline will do, just to remind you of the things you want to talk about; sometimes you may want to jot down key phrases or important statements more fully. But don't write out your whole speech, even as a preliminary step. If you do, some of the written-language patterns may carry over into your talk.

Your manner on the platform should be dignified, yet natural. Perhaps it is idle for us to tell you to be relaxed, because you probably won't be, at least until you have had some experience at addressing gatherings, and perhaps not then. But try to be relaxed; at least try to *look* relaxed.

Speak naturally and with expression, just as you do when you are talking about, let us say, girls. Avoid a monotone; modulate your voice. If you are used to talking with your hands, all right; but don't try to cultivate any special platform gestures.

Enunciate clearly. Do not run your words together; bite them off cleanly. If you are in a room of any size—say as large as a classroom or larger—you will have to speak much louder than you probably think necessary. Most beginning speakers go too fast. Speak slowly. If you have planned your speech properly, there will be no hurry.

Many speakers—including experienced ones—are plagued by the *uh* habit. Like the radio, they cannot seem to tolerate a moment of silence. But instead of filling in the gaps with foolish small talk, they use various forms of the *uh,* long or short. When you have to stop to think of what to say next, don't say *uh;* don't say *anything.* Just maintain a dignified silence, and think. Your listeners will welcome the pause; it will give them a chance to reflect—to catch up with you and consolidate their thoughts.

Always be on guard against random motions. Some speakers have little nervous habits of which they are quite unaware. Popular ones are shaking a piece of chalk as if it were a pair of dice, fiddling with the pointer, and alternately bending and unbending a knee. Any such performance is of course fascinating to the audience, but it tends to take their minds off what you are trying to tell them. You should not be stiff; but don't fall victim to any nervous mannerism.

Watch out also for random movement. Don't pace up and down; stay in one place. You will of course sometimes have to move to or from the blackboard or the screen, and these necessary moves usually provide enough exercise and variety. If you feel that a change is really necessary, take not more than one or two steps forward or backward. You want your audience to be interested in what you are saying, not where you are going.

Look at your audience. Let your eyes move slowly around the room, not neglecting the back rows. Look at your notes only as long as you need to. Be particularly careful not to let your eyes be drawn to the blackboard or the screen longer than necessary to orient yourself. Find the point on the blackboard you want to talk about, point to it, and then face your audience again, still holding the pointer to the board if necessary. Remember, you are talking to the people out front, not to the diagram on the blackboard.

The kind of blackboard presentation that develops before the eyes of the audience is often very effective, particularly for mathematical subjects. It forces the speaker to go slowly, so that his audience can keep up with him. But don't keep your audience waiting unnecessarily while you make drawings that could just as well have been put on the board ahead of time or that could be presented on slides. And use as few equations as you can.

Slides are a fine way of presenting information if they are well prepared (see Sec. 18.7). Arrange them with your talk so that you don't have to keep turning the lights on and off. That is, keep your slides in a few large groups rather than showing one here, one there. (Occasionally a whole speech is given in the dark, with frequently changed slides to accompany it all the way through.)

Just as a written document benefits by subheads, so a speech benefits by some kind of a signal when a new subject is about to come up. Sometimes a pause will do, sometimes an explicit announcement is called for: "Now I am going to tell you how the cover was welded on."

Whenever you have a serious speaking assignment, you will probably do well to practice your speech before the final presentation. Get a few friends or classmates or colleagues to act as audience and to time you.

Give your speech as realistically as you can, and ask for comments and suggestions. Adjust the length to fit the allowed time. (This will practically always mean removing material from your first version.) Repeat the process until you and your trial audience are satisfied with the manner and the length of the presentation, but try to keep the repetitions to a minimum to avoid inadvertent memorization.

Finally, a word about impersonality (see Sec. 13.13). Spoken language is generally less formal than written language. As a result, the devices used to avoid the words *I* and *we* sound even more strained and artificial in a speech than they do in a report or an article. Sometimes you hear a talk that contains several references to "the speaker." Only after you have heard the phrase several times do you realize that the speaker is talking about himself, not some other speaker. Hardly any speech is such a formal occasion that you cannot speak of yourself as *I,* or of yourself and your co-workers as *we.*

REFERENCES

Speaking Can Be Easy . . . for Engineers, too. Engineers' Council for Professional Development.
Hints to Authors. American Chemical Society.
Information for Authors. American Institute for Electrical Engineers.

PART III

TOOLS AND METHODS

13. WRITING: STYLE

The principles expounded in this chapter apply particularly to technical writing. We happen to think that they apply as well to practically all other sorts of writing; but they are here directed specifically to the technical writer.

13.1 Simplicity

Remember that the primary objective of technical writing is to transmit information efficiently. The only writing style suited to this objective is simple, direct, and unadorned. Don't get the idea that an elaborate or elegant style will impress people with your erudition. For every reader impressed by bombast, ten will be annoyed or even left wondering what you are trying to say. People have neither the time nor the inclination to dig out the meaning of unnecessarily obscure prose.

In every technical reporting job, then, say things just as simply, just as directly, just as clearly as you can. Never let your sentences get involved. Don't try to impress your reader; try to tell him something.

The rest of this chapter is devoted to some specific ways of keeping your style simple, direct, and clear.

13.2 Simple Language

The first step to take toward a simple, clear style is to use simple language. Other things being equal, always choose:

(1) A short word rather than a long word.

(2) A plain, familiar word rather than a fancy, unusual word.

(3) A concrete word or a strong verb rather than an abstract word.

Lest these rules sound too categorical, notice the *other-things-being-equal* qualification. If the long word expresses your meaning better than the short word, use it. If the unusual word is more precise than the familiar word, use it. If the abstract word fits the sentence better than the concrete word, use it. But be sure, before you choose the long word or the fancy word, that your intended readers have a reasonable likelihood of knowing it.

The rest of this section consists of examples to illustrate the three rules stated above. Each original example is a negative one—an illustration of what happens when the rules are broken. Each suggested revision shows *one way* of improving the original version. You may very well be able to think of better ways.

13.2.1 The Short Word

Original Example	Suggested Revision
The regulations *prescribe* three formulas *whereby* 95-percent alcohol is *rendered* unfit for consumption.	The regulations *give* three formulas *by which* 95-percent alcohol is *made* unfit for consumption.
We expect to *commence* work on this project immediately.	We expect to *start* work on this project immediately.
The agreement was *effected.*	The agreement was *made.*
Consumption by the synthetic-rubber and explosives industries became almost negligible at the *conclusion* of 1945.	Consumption by the synthetic-rubber and explosives industries became almost negligible at the *end* of 1945.

13.2.2 The Plain (or Familiar) Word

Original Example	Suggested Revision
All persons working near these tubes should be *cognizant* of the danger of explosion.	*Everybody* working near these tubes should be *aware* of the danger of explosion.

Original Example	Suggested Revision
We have no data *pertaining to* airplane traffic.	We have no data *on* airplane traffic.
Workers in the industry have *been desirous of improving* their wages.	Workers in the industry have *wanted to improve* their wages.
Statistical range is used here because it *renders itself* easier to calculate than the standard deviation.	Statistical range is used here because it *is* easier to calculate than the standard deviation.
After the grass has become established, the rye should be *extirpated*.	After the grass has become established, the rye should be *eliminated*.

13.2.3 The Concrete Word

In general, concrete nouns name objects or things that can be perceived by the senses; abstract nouns name qualities, ideas, or conditions that are conceptions of the mind. Abstract nouns tend to be general and vague. In addition, there is a difference in force between nouns and verbs; for the most part, verbs show action and are more vital. As a result, expressions that contain abstract nouns are less forceful, less direct, less exact than their concrete counterparts, and certainly abstract nouns are much less forceful than verbs incorporating the same ideas.

Original Example	Suggested Revision
Control over the size of the voltage increments can be effected by variations of R_1.	The size of the voltage increments can be controlled by variations of R_1.
The tensometers were removed before the *advent* of large deformations.	The tensometers were removed before large deformations occurred.
There is adequate *access* to the job for men and materials.	Men and materials can reach the job readily.
Production engineers have found direct *control* of this operation to be a *necessity*.	Production engineers have found that this operation must be directly controlled.
After *setting* or *stabilization* of the mixture has taken place, the bars are removed from the molds.	After the mixture has set or stabilized, the bars are removed from the molds.
The *need* for instruments that are impervious to atmospheric conditions has long existed.	Instruments that are impervious to atmospheric conditions have long been needed.
The *accuracy* of a large rotor, which gives a less intense field, is much greater.	A larger rotor, which gives a less intense field, is much more accurate.

Original Example	Suggested Revision
The same objection *is applicable* to other proposed designs.	The same objection applies to other proposed designs.
Because of the *limitation* on the *availability* of the bridge ...	Because the bridge was unavailable ...
The reasons for this *popularity* are the almost universal *availability* of slide projectors and the relative *simplicity* of *preparation* of slide originals.	Slides are popular because they are easy to prepare and because slide projectors are almost universally available.

13.2.4 Short, Plain, Concrete, and Action Words

By now you have probably noticed that there is a close connection between short words, plain words, concrete words, and action words. When you choose a plain word, you are likely to get a short one; when you choose a concrete word, you are likely to get a plain one. In Secs. 13.2.1, 13.2.2, and 13.2.3 these factors are treated separately in order to make you recognize all of them. But writers who make the mistake of departing from simple language and action words usually use words that are long and unfamiliar and abstract.

The following examples do not differentiate between our three kinds of fancy language. The revised versions contain shorter, plainer, more concrete, and more action-filled words than the originals; you should find them clearer and easier to read.

Original Example	Suggested Revision
The filled land has gradually compacted, and now there is no *likelihood* of further *subsidence*.	The filled land has gradually compacted, and it is not likely to sink any further.
The department continued to *manifest* unusual *activity*.	The department continued to be unusually active.
One of the puzzling problems in the study of behavior pathology is that of the criteria of the norm from which the pathological manifestations are supposed to deviate.	The study of abnormal behavior is complicated by the absence of accepted standards for normal behavior.
In the coming year his assignment to the investigation is visualized.	He will probably be assigned to the investigation next year.
Measurement of the single-phase reactive component of electrical energy can be *accomplished by the use of a* modified watt-hour meter.	The single-phase reactive component of electrical energy can be measured with a modified watt-hour meter.

Original Example	Suggested Revision
The initiative and enthusiasm requisite to ultimate success of the program must perforce come from the employees.	If the program is to succeed, the employees must enter into it enthusiastically.
Removal of the protecting group from the resulting phthalyl peptide *is effected* by treatment with hydrazine hydrate.	The protecting group is removed from the resulting phthalyl peptide by treatment with hydrazine hydrate.
The amplifier has been used continuously, but the reliability of operation that is desired has not been achieved.	The amplifier has been used continuously, but it has not been sufficiently reliable.
Continuing collaboration between management and labor will prove to be an important element in the implementation of the program.	Continuing collaboration between management and labor will help to keep the program working effectively.
Hypothetically, it may be stated that it is impossible to exactly duplicate the calibration or fabrication of any device. There is always some variability, and it is this variability that enables one to get a perspective of what can be expected of a product.	No device can ever be exactly duplicated, and neither can its calibration. The variability that exists provides a prediction of what can be expected of a product.

13.2.5 Dictionaries

A good dictionary is an essential tool for technical writing. It will help you choose suitable words, and it will be useful for several other purposes (see Secs. 14.10 and 15.1). By all means have one at your side and consult it freely whenever you write. Particularly recommended are *Webster's New Collegiate Dictionary* (Merriam) and *The American College Dictionary* (Harper or Random House). A very useful adjunct is *Webster's Dictionary of Synonyms* (Merriam). The value of this book is probably less in supplying synonyms (see Sec. 13.10) than in distinguishing the small differences between words with similar meanings.

13.3 Elimination of Unnecessary Words

The second step toward a simple, clear style is to eliminate from your writing every word that does not contribute to the meaning or the clarity of your message. Superfluous words are undesirable for three reasons: (1) they waste time (and paper); (2) they obscure significant words and ideas; (3) they rob statements of vigor, force, effectiveness. By all means cut them out, even though the process requires extensive rewriting.

This rule does not, of course, imply that you should write in "telegraphic" style—that you should omit the little words like articles, prepositions, and pronouns that your reader can supply from his own knowledge. You must retain these words, because they help your reader to understand you clearly and easily. They contribute to your message even though it could be deciphered without them.

Most of the unnecessary words in technical writing seem to fall into the three categories illustrated in the following three subsections.

13.3.1 Completely Superfluous Words

You will often see passages containing words that are completely superfluous—words that contribute no meaning whatever. Such deadwood should have no place in your writing. Sometimes these words can simply be struck out; sometimes their removal requires more or less recasting.

You will see that some of the examples below contain unwieldy relative clauses beginning with *which* and *that*. Others reveal trite patterns such as *in the case of*. Probably these constructions were useful at one time; now they are unnecessary.

Original Example	Suggested Revision
The parts *which are* in the warehouse can be shipped immediately. Those *which are* still in process will be ready in two weeks.	The parts in the warehouse can be shipped immediately. Those still in process will be ready in two weeks.
A precipitate forms in containers *that are* left undisturbed overnight.	A precipitate forms in containers left undisturbed overnight.
Significant information on vacuum-tube life has been obtained from records of tubes *which have been* used in the amplifier.	Significant information on vacuum-tube life has been obtained from the records of tubes used in the amplifier.
In *the case of* circular flight, a constant bank angle is desirable.	In circular flight, a constant bank angle is desirable.

Original Example	Suggested Revision
Measurements were also taken with a second probe at the center of the discharge. *In this case* the probe was surrounded by a guard ring as before.	Measurements were also taken with a second probe at the center of the discharge. The probe was surrounded by a guard ring as before.
Only seals *which are of the* hermetic *type* give complete protection.	Only hermetic seals give complete protection.
The purpose of this report is to present the pertinent findings of a job-site inspection *with a view toward* facilitating the erection of the XYZ Building.	This report presents the pertinent findings of a job-site inspection in order to facilitate the erection of the XYZ Building.
A crystal rectifier has been connected across the field to reduce *the magnitude* of the voltage.	A crystal rectifier has been connected across the field to reduce the voltage.
A 10-inch reservoir *is placed* between the main stopcock and the oil diffusion pump. *This* permits operation of the diffusion pump *to be* continued in the event that a short-term shutdown of the forepump *becomes necessary.*	A 10-inch reservoir between the main stopcock and the oil diffusion pump permits continued operation of the diffusion pump in the event of a short-term shutdown of the forepump.
This knowledge is of particular importance in the operation of a system like the one described in this report. *This can be realized when attention is directed to the fact that* a single error can render such a system worthless.	This knowledge is of particular importance in the operation of a system like the one described in this report, *because* a single error can make such a system worthless.
The resulting chart is reproduced in Fig. 6. The average readings of the last period *can be seen to be* approaching the limit line.	The resulting chart is reproduced in Fig. 6. The average readings of the last period approach the limit line.
Figures 6 and 7 show oscillograms of the switching operations, and *it can be seen* that the error is only a few microseconds.	Oscillograms of the switching operations, Figures 6 and 7, show that the error is only a few microseconds.

13.3.2 Circumlocutions

A circumlocution is a roundabout expression—an expression that uses several words to express an idea that can be expressed in fewer words or in one word. Occasionally a circumlocution is desirable: if, for example, your audience is not likely to know its single-word equivalent.

(Should we have said *roundabout expression* instead of *circumlocution*?)
But usually circumlocutions just get in the way. Try to avoid them.

Original Example	Suggested Revision
For this reason, a steam plant is the Company's main source of power.	*Therefore,* a steam plant is the Company's main source of power.
Independent suspension of the front wheels is desirable *due to the fact that* it permits softer front springs to be used.	Independent suspension of the front wheels is desirable *because* it permits softer front springs to be used.
Despite the fact that wages are high in the textile industry, unions are strong.	*Although* wages are high in the textile industry, unions are strong.
To *make an approximation as to how much* time it might take to establish deflection, the following equation is useful.	To *estimate* the time it might take to establish deflection, the following equation is useful.
It is in recognition of this fact that our vacuum-system bores are as large as other practical considerations permit.	*Therefore* our vacuum-system bores are as large as other practical considerations permit.
Leaving out of consideration the size of the tube sealed to the system . . .	*Disregarding* the size of the tube sealed to the system . . .
The tensile strength of grey cast iron differs from the compressive strength *by an extremely large amount.*	The tensile strength of grey cast iron differs *markedly* from the compressive strength.
The nature of the product *is such as to fully negate the feasibility of* an automatic process.	The nature of the product *precludes* an automatic process.
Although *the greatest percent* of the cameras are sold outside of the industry . . .	Although *most* of the cameras are sold outside of the industry . . .
The following charts *add proof to* this statement.	The following charts *corroborate* this statement.

13.3.3 Indirect Expressions

Under this heading we have grouped several constructions that have
two characteristics in common: (1) they say things indirectly and weakly
rather than directly and vigorously; (2) they use more words than their
direct equivalents.

When you look at the examples, you will see that many of the indirect
expressions begin with pronouns followed by weak verbs. Such construc-

tions throw sentences out of balance, leaving the emphatic parts until the
end. Begin your sentences as vigorously as possible.

Original Example	Suggested Revision
There are three basic requirements *that* a saw-tooth sweep signal must fulfill. *These are:* (1)..., (2)..., (3)....	A saw-tooth sweep signal must fulfill three basic requirements: (1)..., (2) ..., (3)....
There are approximately 7000 persons *who* reach their tenth birthday daily in the United States.	Every day about 7000 children in the United States reach their tenth birthday.
There is a city-owned pier running out from this land *which is* used by a marine-repair firm.	A city-owned pier running out from this land is used by a marine-repair firm.
It was probably because of this increased demand *that* the WPB declared cadmium a critical material.	Probably because of this increased demand, the WPB declared cadmium a critical material.
It might be expected *that there would be* some interference to the television channels.	Some interference to the television channels might be expected.
It is essential that the requirements of all the control systems with which the switch may be used be taken into consideration.	The requirements of all the control systems with which the switch may be used *must* be taken into consideration.
It is felt that the derivations of these equations will be interesting to those who have been working on the problem.	The derivations of these equations *should* be interesting to those who have been working on the problem.
It appears that the synthetic material is better than the natural.	The synthetic material is *apparently* better than the natural.
It should be noted that the amount of brightwork was increased despite shortages of copper and nickel.	*Note* that the amount of brightwork was increased despite shortages of copper and nickel.

Is the imperative too blunt? Probably not; but you might have to
soften it in some situations.

It is obvious that the city should increase its reserve water supply.	*Obviously* the city should increase its reserve water supply.
In a triangle with three equal sides *it may be shown that* the three angles are also equai.	In a triangle with three equal sides the three angles are also equal.

It may be shown that is a phrase much used by authors of textbooks
who wish to save space by omitting proofs or derivations. It is also

popular with students who have forgotten proofs or derivations. The phrase may often be omitted. If the reader is familiar with the proof, he doesn't need to be told it exists; if he is not familiar with it, he is not enlightened by the mere statement that it exists. Sometimes *it may be shown that* can be replaced by a more informative or more useful statement, as in the next two examples.

Original Example	Suggested Revision
It may be shown that $\dfrac{V_1}{T_1} = \dfrac{V_2}{T_2}$.	According to Charles' law, $\dfrac{V_1}{T_1} = \dfrac{V_2}{T_2}$.
If these two currents are direct currents, it may be shown that their sum can have only two possible numerical values.	If these two currents are direct currents, by Kirchhoff's first law their sum can have only two possible numerical values.
It is found empirically that the disintegration of a radioactive element follows a simple decay law which states that the rate of decay is proportional to the amount of the radioactive element present.	It is found empirically that the rate of disintegration of a radioactive element is proportional to the amount of the radioactive element present.
In the case of gate-tube studies *it was found that* . . .	Gate-tube studies *demonstrated that* . . .
By looking at the graph on page 20, *one can see that* . . .	The graph on page 20 shows that . . .

Some particularly weak indirect statements that are often used in an overzealous effort to maintain impersonality are illustrated in Sec. 13.13.

13.4 Involved Sentences

Some sentences are difficult to read and understand because they are *involved:* their flow of thought is not straightforward. Involved writing may result from the elementary error of sentence elements in the wrong order (see Sec. 14.3); long sentences are more likely to be involved than short ones (see Secs. 13.5 and 13.6). But short sentences can be involved too, and often involvement is a generally muddy quality that is hard to analyze. One kind of involved sentence in particular that seems to plague the technical writer is the sentence containing a large number of prepositions, especially the preposition *of.*

When you are reading over your rough drafts, watch out for sentences like these.

Original Example	Suggested Revision
Often the ratio of stress concentration here to that elsewhere runs as high as or higher than 3:1.	Often the stress concentration at these points runs 3 times or more as high as it does elsewhere in the specimen.
Above 450 C, the silver content was found not to be constant as was expected.	Contrary to expectations, the silver content was found not to be constant above 450 C.
The most recent method is that of Evans and Goodman, which involves the volumetric determination of helium in a rock sample and measurement of the decay constant by measuring the rate of production of alpha particles, which are the only source of helium in rocks.	The most recent method is that of Evans and Goodman. In this method the volume of helium in a rock sample is determined; then the decay constant is determined through a measurement of the rate of production of alpha particles (the only source of helium in rocks).
Thus the importance of composition is shown if it is assumed that the other variables which may affect the quality of a sinter were held constant and were of such a value as to produce, in conjunction with the proper composition, a superior sinter.	If it is assumed that the other variables were proper and constant, this test demonstrated the importance of composition to the quality of a sinter.
The properties of electromagnetic propagation in a long wire of a transmission system is the subject of this paper.	This paper discusses the properties of electromagnetic propagation in transmission systems containing a long circular wire.
The roasting technique was not as effective as was expected and needs further investigation in order that the factors which prevented the attainment of the quality of roast desired may be determined.	The roasting operation left more sulfur in the sample than was expected. The technique needs further investigation to determine the factors that prevented a satisfactory roast.

13.5 Supercharged Exposition

We have used the adjective *supercharged* to describe exposition that has been pumped too full of meaning, so that the reader has difficulty in containing it and conquering it. The next two subsections illustrate two kinds of supercharged exposition. The second of these is more frequent and more dangerous than the first.

13.5.1 Too Much Pruning

In a worthy zeal to eliminate words (see Sec. 13.3), the technical writer sometimes boils down a statement until it contains insufficient information. The remedy is to complete the explanation; or perhaps occasionally to add words just to dilute a passage that is too concentrated for human consumption.

Original Example	Suggested Revision
On the west the watershed is more centrally located rather than near the southern coast as in the east.	On the west *side of the island* the watershed is more centrally located, rather than *being* near the southern coast as *it is* on the east *side*.
Progress is being made *to show* no significant difference between the variability from day to day and within the day.	Progress is being made *toward a demonstration that there is* no significant difference between the variability from day to day and *the variability* within the day.
The results are shown in Fig. 3. The curves point up the great increase in the maximum conductivity and the gradual shifting of the maximum in the direction of the more concentrated solutions.	Fig. 3 presents a family of curves of conductivity vs. concentration at four different temperatures. Notice that there is a maximum conductivity for each temperature. Also, as the temperatures increase, the conductivity curves are higher and the maximum is displaced in the direction of the more concentrated solutions.

13.5.2 The Long Sentence

A long sentence that flows smooth and straight—a sentence that is not involved—can still contain so much information that the reader's mind can't keep up with it and can't assimilate its information. The remedy for this kind of supercharged exposition is to break the long sentences up into pieces of more easily digestible size. This process often requires the addition of a few accessory words.

Original Example	Suggested Revision
When the input circuit is short-circuited, both the thermal noise and the induced grid noise are reduced to zero, so that the change in noise level in the output of a receiver that is operating linearly gives directly the fraction of shot noise and by inference (given information on the noise figure that can be attained) the proportion of the other two components.	When the input circuit is short-circuited, both the thermal noise and the induced grid noise are reduced to zero. The resulting change in noise level in the output of a receiver that is operating linearly gives the fraction of shot noise. By inference (given information on the noise figure that can be attained), it also shows the proportion of the other two components.

Original Example	Suggested Revision
Suppose a collection of vectors is such that the sum of any two vectors of the collection also belongs to the collection, and such that the scalar product of any vector of the collection with any real number is a vector belonging to the collection.	Suppose that a collection of vectors satisfies two conditions: (1) the sum of any two of the vectors is also a member of the collection; (2) the scalar product of any vector of the collection and any real number is a vector belonging to the collection.
If we recall that the points of a plane can be represented by a couple of numbers (x, y), where x is the distance of the point to the right of an arbitrary origin and y is the distance above that origin, we can represent vectors in the plane as a couple of numbers (x, y), provided we put the rear ends of the vectors at the origin, since vectors may be moved in space unchanged so long as their direction is not altered.	Let us recall two propositions: (1) Any point of a plane can be represented by a couple of numbers, x, y (x is the distance of the point to the right of an origin, y the distance above that origin). (2) Vectors may be moved in space unchanged so long as their direction is not altered. Therefore, if we put its rear end at the origin, we can represent any vector in the plane by a couple of numbers, x, y.

13.6 Varied Sentence Length

You have seen in Secs. 13.4 and 13.5 that long sentences can be very troublesome to the reader if they are involved or if they contain too much high-powered information. Indeed, a current school of thought holds that any prose with an average sentence length of more than 17 words is difficult for the average reader to understand. But for two reasons you should probably vary the length of your sentences, mixing in a few long ones with the short ones: (1) Some of the concepts you will write about are too big or too complex to be expressed in very short sentences. (2) An uninterrupted succession of short, declarative sentences produces a very unpleasant and monotonous effect.

Caution: If you are unable to write long sentences that are clear and uninvolved, by all means stick to short ones. It is better to be clear and jerky than obscure and smooth. And don't overdo the admixture of long sentences.

Here are some examples of jerky, short sentences that can easily be combined and smoothed out with no serious increase in difficulty.

Original Example	Suggested Revision
It is a single-family dwelling of two stories and has an adjoining garage. The house is 36 feet long and 24 feet wide. The joists are lapped and sit on top of the sills, girders, and plates. The joists are bridged with 1 x 3 bridging every 6 feet. The roof is a hip roof and has a slope of 9/12. All sheathing is 10-inch square-edged boards. Many ¼-inch cracks were left between the boards. The firestopping between all joists is brick laid in mortar. It extends 5 inches up into the walls.	The house is a single-family dwelling of two stories, 36 feet long and 24 feet wide, with an adjoining garage. The joists, which are lapped, sit on top of the sills, girders, and plates, and are bridged with 1 x 3 bridging every 6 feet. The roof is a hip roof with a slope of 9/12. All sheathing is 10-inch square-edge boards, with many ¼-inch cracks between them. The firestopping between all joists—brick laid in mortar—extends 5 inches up into the walls.
The coke available was too large to use with good results. The crews broke the coke into usable pieces with hammers. Different particle sizes in the charges were tried. The chemical analysis of all the cokes was the same. The ash content was 11 percent.	Since the coke available was too large to use with good results, the crews broke it into usable pieces with hammers. Different particle sizes in the charges were tried. The chemical analysis of all the cokes was the same, and the ash content was 11 percent.

13.7 The Passive

Every textbook on composition stresses the idea that the passive voice is less vigorous and less effective than the active. Its use is likely to result in wordy, indirect, vague passages. Yet in technical writing the passive inevitably appears a great deal, because of the requirement for impersonality (a requirement that is much exaggerated; see Sec. 13.13). As a result, many technical writers get into the habit of using the passive much more than they need to. Your writing will be clearer and more forceful if you say everything you can in the active rather than the passive.

Here are some examples of conventional passive statements and their active equivalents. In the first one, notice that the use of the passive leaves important gaps in the information transmitted. *Who* developed the first ultracentrifuge? *Who* was working on the development of a semiautomatic machine?

Original Example	Suggested Revision
Studies by Svedberg in 1924 showed that for a high-speed centrifuge the sample must be sector-shaped and protected from the heat of the machine. The first true ultracentrifuge was constructed. It produced a centrifugal force equal to 5000 times the force of gravity. This machine was employed by Svedberg in 1925 to determine the molecular weight of proteins. During these experiments work was being done on the development of a semiautomatic machine that would produce fields as high as 100,000 g.	Svedberg demonstrated in 1924 that for a high-speed centrifuge the sample must be sector-shaped and protected from the heat of the machine. He then constructed the first true ultracentrifuge. It produced a centrifugal force equal to 5000 times the force of gravity. Svedberg employed this machine in 1925 to determine the molecular weight of proteins, and during these experiments he was working on the development of a semiautomatic machine that would produce fields as high as 100,000 g.
Reports have been presented by several members.	Several members have presented reports.
The protecting group is removed from the resulting phthalyl peptide by treatment with hydrazine hydrate.	Treatment with hydrazine hydrate removes the protecting group from the resulting phthalyl peptide.

For examples of some very weak passives used in order to achieve impersonality, see Sec. 13.13, page 141.

13.8 Technical Jargon or Shoptalk

The term *jargon* is used to describe two different kinds of language, one of them much more objectionable than the other. In its broad sense, jargon is any loose, fuzzy, unintelligible talk or writing. For an amusing, eloquent, and wordy plea against this kind of jargon, see the chapter "On Jargon" in Sir Arthur Quiller-Couch's *On the Art of Writing*.

In a narrower sense, jargon is the specialized technical vocabulary peculiar to any trade, science, profession, or special group of people. This kind of jargon—it might better be called *shoptalk*—is often condemned wholesale, along with the other kind. The main drawback of shoptalk is that it is a "secret" language: an engineer will not understand a physician's shoptalk any more than a physician will understand a bricklayer's. Indeed, it is this very secrecy that makes shoptalk appeal to some people (think of the conversation of some radio amateurs).

But shoptalk very often expresses in one word a large concept that would require many words, or even sentences, from the general vocabulary. For instance, when the electrical engineer says that he has constructed a *breadboard* of a newly designed circuit, his brothers in the trade know that he has put together a preliminary model containing the functional components of his final circuit, but that these components have not been laid out with an eye to neat or compact design; that what will be single units in the final circuit are probably built up from proper combinations of several units available in the stock room; that what will be fixed values in the final circuit are probably adjustable; and that the connections are temporary.

If he is talking to his colleagues, this electrical engineer would be foolish to spend the time and words necessary to avoid the use of *breadboard*. On the other hand, if he is addressing laymen, he would be wasting his time to speak of a breadboard, because they wouldn't know what he was talking about.

This discussion of shoptalk might be generalized into two rules:

(1) When a term from the general vocabulary expresses your idea as well and as economically as a shoptalk term, always choose the general term.

(2) Even if a shoptalk term is more precise or more economical than a general term, don't use it unless you are sure that your audience will know it. (When you are going to express the idea repeatedly, you can use the strange term if you define it carefully at its first appearance.)

Of course, slangy shoptalk is as inappropriate as any other slang in formal situations.

Below are several examples of shoptalk that could just as well be expressed in terms from the general vocabulary.

Original Example	Suggested Revision
When such a system is studied *in vitro*, it demonstrates respiratory activity at a rate proportional to the concentrations of these breakdown products. *In vivo*, the concentration is determined by the rate of work being done by the cell.	When such a system is studied *in the test tube*, it demonstrates respiratory activity at a rate proportional to the concentrations of these breakdown products. *In the living cell*, the concentration is determined by the rate of work being done by the cell.
The new engine *peaks* at 5500 rpm.	The new engine *produces its maximum horsepower* at 5500 rpm.
The mixture was stirred, and bromine was added *dropwise*.	The mixture was stirred, and bromine was added *by drops*.

Original Example	Suggested Revision
In the usual commercial acceptance procedure, a tensile test is *pulled*.	In the usual commercial acceptance procedure, a tensile test is *performed*.
Surface water drains through the grass in a *northeasterly direction* across the *southwesterly* sidewalk of Broadway.	Surface water drains through the grass *toward the northeast* across the *southwest* sidewalk of Broadway.
The hydrogen is converted by another series of *stepwise* reactions.	The hydrogen is converted by another series of *step-by-step* reactions.

Several years ago Arthur D. Little, Inc., a consulting engineering firm of Cambridge, Massachusetts, published an issue of their *Technical Bulletin* called "The Turbo-Encabulator," which received wide circulation and was even reprinted in a popular weekly magazine. Here is the opening paragraph:

> For a number of years now work has been proceeding in order to bring to perfection the crudely conceived idea of a machine that would not only supply inverse reactive current for use in unilateral phase detractors, but would also be capable of automatically synchronizing cardinal grammeters. Such a machine is the "Turbo-Encabulator." Basically, the only new principle involved is that instead of power being generated by the relative motion of conductors and fluxes, it is produced by the modial interaction of magneto-reluctance and capacitive directance.

"The Turbo-Encabulator" is the *reductio ad absurdum* of technical jargon. It is full of specially composed, trumped-up, absurd technical terms that mean nothing at all. But it sounds so much like many real engineering reports that most laymen could read it without ever finding out that it is a hoax, and many engineers get halfway through it before they discover that their legs are being pulled. Don't let your writing get into the "Turbo-Encabulator" class.

13.9 Clichés

A cliché is a trite, overused expression or combination of words. The cliché is usually a *tricky* phrase that was fresh and vigorous when it was first coined because it involved a certain surprise element. But when such a phrase is used over and over again, it becomes so familiar that it loses all its impact. Like an overplayed phonograph record, it is hardly even heard.

Have you ever noticed that a gaudily decorated night club looks much worse when old and worn than does an unpretentious tool shed? Similarly the overused cliché is more noticeable and more unpleasant than the often-repeated everyday expression. Try to avoid figures of speech that have become common. Here are a few examples.

Original Example	Suggested Revision
I shall be *only too glad* to discuss it with you.	I shall be *glad* to discuss it with you.
I wish to thank *each and every one of you.*	I wish to thank *every one* of you.
The brushes can be easily replaced *if and when* they wear out.	The brushes can be easily replaced *if* they wear out.
For any engineer *with his ear to the ground,* Dr. Smith's paper on atomic energy furnishes *food for thought.*	Any engineer alert to the problem of dwindling fuel supplies would find Dr. Smith's paper on atomic energy stimulating and provocative.
Must be seen to be appreciated.	[You better think up something entirely different for this old chestnut.]

13.10 Repetition

At some time during your schooling, you were probably told not to repeat a word within a sentence, or within a paragraph, or within some other unit. This is dangerous advice; you should not take it literally. *It is always better to repeat a word than to becloud your meaning or to sound artificial in avoiding the repetition.* The *contrived variation* can be very confusing:

Original Example	Comment	Suggested Revision
Circuit theory and field theory are complementary disciplines, each very useful. Of the many engineering applications of stereonics, the following may be mentioned.	Even when you have recently been told that *stereonics* is another name for *field theory,* this passage at first reading seems to mention three branches of learning rather than two.	Circuit theory and field theory are complementary disciplines, each very useful. Of the many engineering applications of field theory, the following may be mentioned.

Original Example	Comment	Suggested Revision
It is best to start with a coarse net, even though a fine mesh is the ultimate goal. Successive trials bring the grid lines closer and closer together.	The effort required to correlate *net, mesh,* and *grid* in this passage delays the reader's understanding.	It is best to start with a coarse grid, even though a fine one is the ultimate goal. Successive trials bring the grid lines closer and closer together.
In this collection of vectors, the sum of any two vectors is a member of the set.	Did you realize immediately that *set* was the same as *collection*?	In this collection of vectors, the sum of any two vectors is a member of the collection.
Progress has been defined as the replacement of an old set of problems by a series of entirely new ones.	Did the author mean to differentiate between *set* and *series*? Probably not; but the variation sets us to wondering, and it sounds contrived and artificial.	Progress has been defined as the replacement of an old set of problems by a set of entirely new ones.

It is the repetition of hackneyed phrases and big or unusual words that is objectionable, not the everyday bread-and-butter words. You eat bread and butter with every meal and don't get tired of it; but try that with plum pudding! Consider this excerpt from a paper on the Port of Baltimore:

> Each of the trunk railroads wants to obtain as much traffic as it can with independence from the other carriers, but a certain interchange of traffic is necessary. It is believed that the existing lighterage system allows this interchange with the least capital expenditure.
>
> It is believed that there are four pieces of land in the port having possibilities for development as ship terminals.
>
> The Hawkins Point land is owned by the Patapsco Land Co. Being adjacent to the Davison Chemical Co. plant, it has railroad connections. It is primarily open land and is within the lighterage limits of the harbor.
>
> It is believed that this section is not entirely satisfactory, for the following reasons:
>
> 1. It is too far from the business center of town and the existing piers and warehouses.
>
> 2. It is served by only one railroad.
>
> 3. It is believed that for the best interests of the industrial development of the city, outlying land of this type should be used by industry.

You probably noticed that *It is believed that* occurs four times in this passage, and you were probably annoyed by it. (The phrase could be

eliminated all four times: the first statement might then be softened by
"The . . . system *seems* to allow . . ."; the second by "Four pieces
. . . *show* possibilities. . . .") But did you notice that the word *land*
occurs five times? And that *traffic* appears twice in one sentence, and
the businesslike *interchange* in successive sentences?

The repetition of even a short, everyday word can become monotonous if it is overdone:

Original Example	Suggested Revision
Although cadmium has been known as a metal since 1817, practically it is one of the younger metals because its use has not been fully explored and developed. Until the early 1920's there were only a few uses for cadmium, and its occurrence in ores was looked on solely as a nuisance. When it was discovered that the metal could be recovered as a by-product in the electrolytic zinc process, no use was known for it, and early attempts to substitute it for tin were unsuccessful. Later its valuable properties in rust-proof coatings on steel became known, and then followed its use in high-pressure bearing alloys. More uses were found for the metal, and its importance increased rapidly; in 1941, the consumption of cadmium reached nearly 4000 tons in the United States alone. Even then the demand was so great that it was placed on the list of critical materials for war uses, and its use was restricted by the War Production Board.	Although cadmium has been known as a metal since 1817, practically it is one of the younger metals because its applications have not been fully explored and developed. Until the early 1920's there were only a few uses for cadmium, and its occurrence in ores was looked on solely as a nuisance. When it was discovered that the metal could be recovered as a by-product in the electrolytic zinc process, no use was known for it, and early attempts to substitute it for tin were unsuccessful. Later its valuable properties in rust-proof coatings on steel became known, and then followed its use in high-pressure bearing alloys. More applications were found for the metal, and its importance increased rapidly; in 1941, the consumption of cadmium reached nearly 4000 tons in the United States alone. Even then the demand was so great that it was placed on the list of critical war materials, and its consumption was restricted by the War Production Board.
Well over half of the cadmium produced is used for the electroplating of other metals. The aircraft and automotive industries, which are the principal consumers, use a large number of cadmium-plated bolts and parts.	Well over half the cadmium produced goes into the electroplating of other metals. The aircraft and automotive industries, which are the principal consumers, employ a large number of cadmium-plated bolts and parts.

The word *use* appears nine times in the original example, three times
in the revision. Yet the variations do not seem contrived.

Repetition is particularly objectionable when the repeated word stands

for two different ideas. This kind of repetition is not just monotonous;
it is confusing.

Original Example	Suggested Revision
Smith went to some *pains* to make the revision as *painless* as possible.	Smith went to some *trouble* to make the revision as *painless* as possible.
Fuel density *varies* with temperature. Although there is some *variation* in different grades of gasoline, the value of 0.1 percent per degree centigrade is typical.	Fuel density *varies* with temperature. Although the *variation* is not the same for all grades of gasoline, the value of 0.1 percent per degree centigrade is typical.

Varies refers to density. The original *variation* refers to differences
between fuels. *Variation* in the revised version refers, again, to density.

In summary: try to avoid monotonous repetition; but always use the
best, the clearest word you can find, repetition or no repetition.

13.11 Footnotes (Explanatory)

You may wonder why a discussion of footnotes (the further-explanation kind) appears under the heading of "Writing: Style" rather than
under "Mechanics," along with the treatment of citation or reference
footnotes in Sec. 16.6. We have chosen to talk about explanatory
footnotes here because they have a pronounced effect on style and general tone and clarity.

Every footnote is a digression from the main stream of thought. It
interrupts the reader. If he reads it, his eyes must make an excursion
to the bottom of the page (or to the end of the chapter); and when he
is through, he must find the place where he departed from the main text.
Lengthy footnotes can cause the reader to lose the thread of your message, to miss what you are trying to tell him. Even short footnotes are
at best a nuisance. Use as few of them as you can.

When we borrow the words or the ideas of somebody else, we must
give credit for them. Reference footnotes furnish a convenient and
unobtrusive way of fulfilling this obligation. Most people do not bother
to read them except occasionally.

But explanatory footnotes can practically never be justified on the
grounds of necessity. Most of them can be blamed on one of two factors: (1) the writer has the mistaken notion that a lot of footnotes will

make his discourse look learned or scholarly or elegant; (2) the writer has not taken the trouble to organize his material thoroughly, and he finds that he has some good ideas that do not fit readily into his main text.

We believe that practically all the customary further-explanation footnotes should either be integrated into the main text or relegated to the wastebasket (or perhaps put in an appendix). Whenever you find yourself with some leftover comments that you are tempted to put into a footnote, evaluate them carefully. If they really contribute to your theme, take the trouble to work them into the text (perhaps in parenthesis, if they are of secondary importance). If they are not worth this much trouble, don't bother your reader with them at all.

Here is a brief example of a footnote that can easily be moved to the text, where it is much less of an interruption.

Original Example	Suggested Revision
The resultant voltage induced around a loop* by an incident wave is found as follows. Voltages induced in the vertical members are equal to . . .	The resultant voltage induced around a loop by an incident wave is found as follows. (A square loop is assumed. A round loop would be reduced to an equivalent square.) Voltages induced in the vertical members are equal to . . .

Particularly annoying is an undifferentiated mixture of citation footnotes and explanatory footnotes. Confronted by such a mixture, the reader who is in the habit of ignoring citation footnotes is likely to miss essential information in the explanatory footnotes; or the conscientious reader who doesn't want to skip any worthwhile information finds himself being continually interrupted by purely routine citations.

13.12 Subordination

A common failing of technical writers is to express ideas of unequal importance in constructions that seem to give them equal weight. Your readers will grasp your meaning more quickly and more easily if you indicate subordinate ideas by putting them in subordinating constructions. At the same time, you will probably eliminate some unnecessary

---

* A square loop is assumed. A round loop would be reduced to an equivalent square.

words, and you will relieve your style from the monotony of a succession
of simple declarative sentences.

In the first example, the more important idea is that the figures represent the energy consumed each year; the fact that the figures are in
kilowatt-hours should be subordinated to the main idea and take second
place.   A good general rule is that whenever you write a sentence with
the ideas joined together by *and* or *so*, see if it wouldn't be improved by
subordination.

Original Example	Suggested Revision
These figures are in kilowatt-hours and represent the energy consumed each year.	These figures (in kilowatt-hours) represent the energy consumed each year.
This value is best determined by actual test and is 50 watts.	This value, best determined by actual test, is 50 watts.
Sand is the other important raw material and is procured from an outside supplier.	Sand, the other important raw material, is procured from an outside supplier.
The maximum obtainable temperature was found to be 1800 F and was maintained throughout ⅔ the length of the tube.	The maximum obtainable temperature, which was found to be 1800 F, was maintained throughout ⅔ the length of the tube.
This estimate has been plotted in Fig. 3 and shows the likelihood that the meters will all fail at the same time.	This estimate, which has been plotted in Fig. 3, shows the likelihood that the meters will all fail at the same time.
Industrial Arts Index is published in New York and it lists periodical articles on technology and commerce.	*Industrial Arts Index*, published in New York, lists periodical articles on technology and commerce.
The cornice detail is simple and is illustrated in Fig. 1.	The cornice detail (illustrated in Fig. 1) is simple.

or:

The simple cornice detail is illustrated
in Fig. 1.

13.13 Impersonality

The last section in this chapter on style is probably one of the most
important and certainly the most controversial.

Most technical reports and papers describe ideas or physical events
or physical objects.   Quite properly, the observations are supposed to be

accurate and objective, and the observer is thrust into the background. When you report on an investigation, your reader is interested in what you found out, not in you. So far, so good.

Based on this perfectly sound notion a convention has grown up that the technical writer must always remain completely impersonal; in particular, that he must never use the first-person singular pronoun, *I*. As a result, most technical reporting is much more impersonal and much drier than it really needs to be. Don't you increase the efficiency of a communication when you make it interesting and pleasant to read? Contrast these two excerpts from departmental reports:

The Impersonal Approach	The Personal Approach
The staff in these trying times, although pressed by routine duties, has nevertheless found time to participate in professional and scholarly activities. Meetings of such professional societies as the American Association for the Advancement of Science and the American Society for Engineering Education have been well attended. In some instances papers have been read, and an appreciable quota of committee appointments have been assigned to Department staff members. The Chairman of the Department has been selected as the editor of a forthcoming symposium of studies relating the various branches of engineering to the general advancement of society.	In the spring of 1951 the Department agreed to make an investigation and report for the government on the development of waterpower facilities. This task enlisted the services of over 50 professional men, including mechanical, civil, and electrical engineers, physicists, and meteorologists. As director of the project, I had unusual opportunity to observe the benefits derived from an enterprise which united outstanding men from several universities and from industry— men with widely differing professional backgrounds but with a common goal.

These excerpts come from reports written and signed by the respective department chairmen. The one in the left column uses the conventional, proper, impersonal approach. It is rather stuffy; you wonder for a moment just who has been attending meetings and reading papers. Is the chairman really being impersonal and modest when he speaks of himself as *the Chairman of the Department*?

The report in the right column relaxes a little from the purely impersonal, third-person approach. To us it is a very refreshing change from the more conventional style. Does the chairman sound egotistical, or does he lose his objective viewpoint, when he speaks of himself as *I*? We think not.

Many technical reports and papers describe work that is so objective that the reader does not care who did it. He wants to know that the work was done, but he is not at all interested in the agency that brought it about. The conventional impersonal passive construction (see Sec. 13.7) is suitable for this kind of subject.

But often—although you are completely objective and suitably modest—you need to introduce the concept of yourself in order to describe the work that you have done or to warn your readers that you are expressing an opinion. If you are slavish about avoiding *I*, you have in general three choices:

(1) You can call yourself *the author*, or *the writer*, or *one*, and talk about yourself in the third person. Now we believe—and a lot of people agree with us—that this construction is highly artificial and that it is in fact no more impersonal than *I*. Furthermore, it is likely to be confusing, because "the author" could be talking about some other author.

(2) You can resort to an extremely weak passive construction in which the doer is unnamed and vague, although his identity is really an essential part of the story.

Original Example	Suggested Revision
The first week of the period was spent on vacation. Work is now continuing on completion of the next annual report. A description of the new high-temperature technique is the item that has come under consideration.	During the first week of the period I was on vacation. I am now writing a description of the new high-temperature technique for the next annual report.
The current period has been devoted to becoming familiarized with the new equipment.	I have spent the current period in becoming familiarized with the new equipment.

These examples illustrate perhaps the most absurd place to be literal about impersonality—the progress report on your own activities. You are talking about yourself, and you may as well admit it.

(3) You can use the weak indirect construction discussed in Sec. 13.3.3.

It is believed that the city should increase its reserve water supply.	I believe that the city should increase its reserve water supply.

Original Example	Suggested Revision
It is desired to ascertain how you succeeded in increasing the yield of low-boiling fractions.	We should like to find out how you increased the yield of low-boiling fractions.
It was a pleasure to talk with you and your staff.	I enjoyed talking with you and your staff.
It is my thinking (thought) that . . .	I think (or believe) that . . .

All three of these alternatives are at best artificial, stilted, and vague; at worst, downright confusing. There is only one natural, direct way to talk about yourself, and that is to say *I.*

Similarly, the natural word to use when you are speaking for a group of people is *we.* Authors of textbooks use *we* very freely to stand for an indefinite body of people that includes the writer and his readers. But *we* meaning the writer and his associates or colleagues is treated with the same prejudice as *I.*

You can sound egotistical and subjective without ever uttering an *I* or a *we.* Conversely, you can maintain the proper tone of modesty and objectivity even though you do say these words. If you will use the first-person construction judiciously, you will often find your writing task eased, because you will be speaking naturally; and your audience will find the result clear and pleasant to read.

Caution: This advice to use the first person must definitely be qualified. Some publications and some organizations have a specific policy forbidding the use of I or we. When you write for such a publication or such an organization, you must of course adhere to their rules (at least, until you have gained a position of sufficient eminence and power to be able to change the rules). In the meantime, don't be *unnecessarily* impersonal.

14. WRITING: GRAMMAR

14.1 An Unpleasant Word

In any treatise on technical reporting, we come inevitably to a subject that we may as well frankly call *grammar*. Technical students (and others too) automatically recoil at the mention of this subject. Many of them take refuge in the popular notion that a direct approach and a lively style are more important than correct grammar.

Now we do not mean to belittle the importance of directness and liveliness. But the fact remains that, other factors being equal, grammatical writing is easier to read and easier to understand than ungrammatical writing. And it is easier not only for the reader who knows the rules himself, but also for the reader who is ignorant of them. For most of the rules of grammar are not simply arbitrary, capricious dictums put out by some old fuddy-duddy in order to trip you up in quizzes; they are, rather, codifications of logical relationships.

You may gather that we are trying to make grammarians out of technical men. This would be an impossible task even if it were a desirable one. But since the principles of grammar will help you communicate information clearly and efficiently, you ought to know at least the more important ones.

Unfortunately, the usual approach to grammar depends heavily on the rote memorization of a lot of formal rules and technical terms. You were probably subjected to this sort of thing in high school or in a freshman composition class. If you are like most students, you resisted this instruction and you have forgotten much of what you learned. Does one have to know what *addend, augend,* and *summand* are to be able to add two numbers together? No. Similarly, is it necessary to learn technical grammatical terms (beyond a few basic ones) to write grammatically? We believe not.

Therefore in this chapter (and the next one, on punctuation) we have relied as much as possible on common sense and logic and rules of thumb. We have tried to keep technical grammatical terms to a minimum and have restricted ourselves to the important rules that technical writers seem to overlook most often.

Thus this is a guide to correct usage, but it is by no means a complete handbook. When you are in doubt about any matter not covered here, look it up in a composition handbook. If you do not already own one, we recommend Porter G. Perrin's *Writer's Guide and Index to English* (Scott, Foresman) and J. D. Thomas's *Composition for Technical Students* (Scribner's). If you are interested in the fine points, investigate H. W. Fowler's *Dictionary of Modern English Usage* (Oxford).

If you can't seem to make a construction come out right even with the aid of a handbook, dodge the issue. Tear up what you have written and start over again with an entirely different construction and a fresh approach.

In the remainder of this chapter and in the next one you will find a number of examples of writing that we have condemned as being *unclear.* You may argue that some of these examples are only momentarily unclear; or that the general sense or logic of the whole passage clarifies them; or that anybody could understand them with a little study. Certainly permanent misunderstanding is worse than temporary misunderstanding. But even momentary misconstruction is a serious handicap to the reader. You owe it to your reader to make your meaning immediately clear with a minimum of study on his part.

14.2 Vague Pronoun

A common fault of technical writers is the use of pronouns whose meaning is vague or confusing. This is a serious fault, because it can result in misunderstanding. *Every pronoun must stand for a word (or an idea) that has already been expressed; and what it stands for must be immediately evident.*

Worst of all, of course, is the pronoun whose meaning cannot be deduced at all.

> These observations do not, however, explain why e_2 does not rise above E_b, and *this* will be important to us.

What will be important? The fact that e_2 fails to rise above E_b, or the fact that our observations do not explain the failure? The sentence contains no clue.

The pronoun whose meaning is momentarily in doubt is less serious, but it slows the reader down, particularly if he has to think things out in order to arrive at the meaning.

> The aluminum-nickel-iron alloys have external magnetic energy values five times those of the best quench-hardening alloys. *These* are carbon-free alloys whose magnetic hardness is controlled by. . . .

Are *these* the aluminum-nickel-iron alloys or the quench-hardening alloys? If the reader happens to be a metallurgist, he knows that *these* stands for the aluminum-nickel-iron alloys, because they are the ones that are carbon-free. But you should never require your reader to do this sort of puzzling even if he is capable of it. Again,

> As the temperature falls, a compressive stress is exerted by the bezel on the glass because of *its* greater temperature coefficient.

Anybody with technical training can figure out that it is the bezel that has the greater temperature coefficient; but why impose this task on your reader? A simple revision will get rid of the ambiguity and the passive construction at the same time:

> As the temperature falls, the bezel, because of its greater temperature coefficient, exerts a compressive stress on the glass.

Still less serious is the vague pronoun whose meaning is revealed as the reader gets further on in the sentence. But even this sort of vagueness makes the reader's task more difficult, and you should always avoid it. The trouble is aggravated when the same pronoun is allowed to stand, in close succession, for two different antecedents. Here are some examples:

Original Example	Suggested Revision
Laminar flow has no corrosive power. *It* is seldom used, because *it* is not economical to use low speeds.	Laminar flow has no corrosive power. It is seldom used, because low speeds are not economical.
This intense specialization is necessary in our industrial society because of *its* complexity. *It* is advantageous because *it* allows an individual to become really proficient in at least one field.	This intense specialization is necessitated by the complexity of our industrial society. It is advantageous because it allows an individual to become really proficient in at least one field.
It became listless during the hot part of the day and revived when *it* got cooler.	It became listless during the hot part of the day and revived when the temperature fell.
This presupposes that the computer is working with continuously recycling problems during the check; but since no intelligible results can be obtained from the check unless *this* is being done, *this* is no limitation.	This presupposes that the computer is working with continuously recycling problems during the check; but since no intelligible results can be obtained from the check unless the problems are recycling, this requirement is no limitation.
This is an unfortunate situation, and *one* exceedingly unpleasant for the honest scientist, and *one* is inclined to feel that the scientist should take no part in such proceedings.	This is an unfortunate situation, and one exceedingly unpleasant for the honest scientist. We believe that the scientist should take no part in such proceedings.
Attempts to build high-compression engines that would operate on low-octane gasoline depended on the theory that if maximum surface temperatures in the combustion chamber could be reduced by 600–1000 F, the mixture temperature could be controlled so that spontaneous ignition would not occur under high compression pressure. *This* required elimination of the exhaust valve, which reaches temperatures as high as 1300 F in automobile engines operating at maximum power.	Attempts to build high-compression engines that would operate on low-octane gasoline depended on the theory that if maximum surface temperatures in the combustion chamber could be reduced by 600–1000 F, the mixture temperature could be controlled so that spontaneous ignition would not occur under high compression pressure. *Such a reduction in surface temperature* required elimination of the exhaust valve, which reaches temperatures as high as 1300 F in automobile engines operating at maximum power.

The purist says that every pronoun must stand for a noun antecedent. In technical writing we can take a more liberal view and let pronouns stand for whole ideas that have been expressed if the reference is perfectly clear. In the following example, the pronoun *this* obviously stands for the whole idea expressed in the sentence that precedes it. To replace *this* by a wordier construction would be pedantic.

> The curve for tubes used in flip-flops lies below the curve for tubes used in other circuits. This indicates that the flip-flop is the severest application for these tubes.

But remember: be sure your reader will be able to tell immediately and without pondering what every pronoun stands for.

14.3 Order of Sentence Elements

An important factor in clear writing is the proper order for the elements that go to make up each sentence. In general, try to *keep operators near the words they operate on*. If you do not, they will seem to operate on the wrong words. Here are some examples:

Original Example	Comments	Suggested Revision
A firm grip on the instrument and a firm support on the jaw of the patient are necessary when the mobilometer is being used to insure correct position, pressure, and steadiness during readings.	. . . the mobilometer is being used to insure correct position . . . ?	To insure correct position, pressure, and steadiness during readings, a firm grip on the instrument and a firm support on the jaw of the patient are necessary when the mobilometer is being used.
This rejection rate indicates that steps will have to be taken to reduce the incidence of short circuits by the manufacturer.	. . . short circuits by the manufacturer?	This rejection rate indicates that the manufacturer will have to take steps to reduce the incidence of short circuits.
Problems of a topographical nature are not likely to arise because the ground is generally flat.	. . . to arise because the ground is . . . flat?	Because the ground is generally flat, problems of a topographical nature are not likely to arise.
Purpose of the experiment was to compare half-wave potentials obtained experimentally for copper and lead in tartrate solutions with accepted literature values.	. . . solutions with accepted literature values?	Purpose of the experiment was to compare with accepted literature values the half-wave potentials obtained experimentally for copper and lead in tartrate solutions.

Original Example	Comments	Suggested Revision
Draw a line through the magnetization curve from the origin having this slope.	. . . the magnetization curve from the origin? . . . the origin having this slope?	Draw a line having this slope from the origin through the magnetization curve.
The effect of vibration and shock is difficult to report for permanent-magnet materials.	. . . to report for permanent-magnet materials?	The effect of vibration and shock on permanent-magnet materials is difficult to report.
The librarian will obtain books that are out of the library for the engineer.	. . . out of the library for the engineer?	The librarian will obtain for the engineer books that are out of the library.
In order to obtain reliable recordings on magnetic tape it appears that there are two factors that can cause loss of information that must be overcome.	. . . information that must be overcome?	Apparently there are two factors that can cause loss of information from magnetic tape. They must both be overcome in order to obtain reliable recordings.
No read-back pulses were obtained by either oscilloscope or ear phones on one channel using 300 feet of tape which could be attributed to tape imperfections.	. . . tape which could be attributed to tape imperfections?	No read-back pulses which could be attributed to tape imperfections were obtained by either oscilloscope or ear phones on 300 feet of one channel.
When the pulse arrives that de-energizes the rotating standard, the relay is opened.		Upon the arrival of the pulse that de-energizes the rotating standard, the relay is opened.
Baseball Commissioner A. B. Chandler opened a hearing on charges that manager Leo Durocher of the New York Giants struck and kicked a fan at the Polo Grounds a half hour ahead of schedule today. —Boston *Globe*	Those big-league ball clubs try to do *everything* according to schedule.	

In particular, try not to separate a verb too far from its subject or its object or complement.

Original Example	Comments	Suggested Revision
No trouble with flip-flops running 700 or 800 hours where balance and tubes were concerned has developed.	No trouble . . . has developed. What kind of trouble? Where balance . . .	No balance or tube trouble has developed with flip-flops running 700 or 800 hours.

If the object or complement of a verb is compound, the apparent separation can be reduced by putting the shorter element nearer the verb:

The new designs were at once suitable for production in the large quantities required and of improved performance.		The new designs were at once of improved performance and suitable for production in the large quantities required.
The use of a-c propulsion with a synchronous motor requires a number of complicated interconnections between units and elaborate control equipment.	. . . interconnection between units and elaborate control equipment?	The use of a-c propulsion with a synchronous motor requires elaborate control equipment and a number of complicated interconnections between units.

The word *only* is very frequently misplaced. In speech or informal usage it is customarily put before the verb. But in technical writing, precision requires it to go immediately before the word it modifies.

This group will only study those problems that require lengthy investigations.	Seems to say that the group will do no more than *study* those problems . . . ; it will not do any actual experimental work.	This group will study only those problems that require lengthy investigations.
Chittagong only competes with Calcutta in the importing of mineral oils.	Could mean that Chittagong competes *only with* Calcutta . . . or that *only Chittagong* competes with Calcutta. . . . The actually intended meaning is made clear in the right-hand column.	Chittagong competes with Calcutta only in the importing of mineral oils.

14.4 Dangling Modifier

The dangling modifier does not often cause the downright confusion of the vague pronoun, but it is highly illogical, and on many readers it creates the same impression as the word *ain't*. Therefore you should avoid it.

Perhaps you have forgotten what a dangling modifier is. In general, it is a modifier that seems, at least momentarily, to operate on the wrong word. It is usually a verb form (often a participle) that is not supplied with a subject in its own sentence element, and that seems to claim a wrong word as its subject. An unfortunate order of sentence elements is often a contributing cause.

Consider this sentence:

> By specifying standardized resistors, the designer can reduce the cost of the chassis.

The word *specifying* in the first part of the sentence is a verb form (it happens to be a gerund, but no matter) with no subject expressed. In the second part of the sentence *the designer* is the subject of *can reduce*. But it also seems to be the subject of *specifying;* and indeed it *is* logically the subject of *specifying*. Who does the specifying? The designer, of course. There is nothing wrong with this construction.

Now consider a similar sentence:

> By specifying standardized resistors, the cost of the chassis can be reduced.

Now *the cost* is in exactly the same situation as *the designer* was in the first sentence. As a result, *the cost* seems momentarily to be the subject of *specifying*. Does the cost do the specifying? No; some unnamed agent does. In this construction *specifying* is said to dangle. It is unattached, but it seems to attach itself to *the cost*.

You can usually correct a dangling modifier in several ways:

(1) By supplying a subject:

> By specifying standardized resistors, *we* can reduce the cost of the chassis.

(2) By changing the verb form to a word that is obviously a noun, and that therefore does not want to claim a subject:

> By *the specification of* standardized resistors, the cost of the chassis can be reduced.

(3) By changing the order of the sentence elements:

> The cost of the chassis can be reduced by specifying standardized resistors.

This construction leaves *specifying* still technically unattached, and the purist may object to it. But because there is no noun in a position where it seems to be claimed as subject, the sentence is not even momentarily illogical or misleading.

(4) By rewriting the sentence completely:

The use of standardized resistors will reduce the cost of the chassis.

The dangling modifier can assume various forms. The following examples should help you to recognize and avoid this blunder.

Original Example	Comments	Suggested Revision
The sentence gains in simplicity and clarity by eliminating superfluous words.	Does the sentence eliminate words?	The sentence gains in simplicity and clarity by the elimination of superfluous words.
By breaking part of the material with the first charges, the following charges expend more of their energy in the direction of the weak point than they would if they were fired at the time of the first charges.	Do the following charges break part of the material with the first charges?	The first charges break part of the material and form a weak point. The following charges expend more of their energy in the direction of this weak point than they would if they were fired at the time of the first charges.
After locating the site, it did not fulfill expectations.	Did it (the site) locate the site?	After being located, the site did not fulfill expectations.
After calibrating the manometer, three patients were found to have high blood pressure.	Did the patients calibrate the manometer?	After the manometer had been calibrated, three patients were found to have high blood pressure.
With the baffle in place, fuel does not splash when flying in rough air.	Is the fuel flying in rough air?	. . . fuel does not splash when the airplane is flying in rough air. *or:* . . . fuel does not splash during flight in rough air.
Combining the two adjustments properly, the jaw speed can be varied from 0.002 inch per minute . . .	Does the jaw speed combine the adjustments?	With the proper combination of the two adjustments, the jaw speed can be varied from 0.002 inch per minute . . .

Original Example	Comments	Suggested Revision
This load curve is plotted so as to show the increasing slope with increasing load. When plotted in this way, additional curves may be drawn parallel to the original curve.	Are the additional curves plotted in this way? Only incidentally; primarily, it is *this load curve* that is plotted in this way.	This load curve is plotted so as to show the increasing slope with increasing load. When it is plotted in this way, additional curves may be drawn parallel to the original curve.
Of itself, the band theory of solids offers an incomplete explanation of ferromagnetism, but when considered jointly with the electron theory, many of the problems confronting us in our investigation can be answered.	Are the problems confronting us considered jointly with the electron theory? No; the band theory of solids is.	Of itself, the band theory of solids offers an incomplete explanation of ferromagnetism, but when *it is* considered jointly with the electron theory, many of the problems confronting us in our investigation can be answered.
The curves for a vacuum tube will indicate the range of voltage over which linear assumptions are justified just by looking at them.	Do the curves look at them (selves)?	A glance at the curves for a vacuum tube will indicate the range of voltage over which linear assumptions are justified.
The meter is not sufficiently sensitive to be able to read the small differences involved.	Should the meter be able to read the differences?	The meter is not sufficiently sensitive *for us* to be able to read the small differences involved.
		or:
		The meter is not sufficiently sensitive *to show* the small differences involved.
In the neighborhood of the crystal's resonant frequency, P. Vigoureaux has derived the following values for the parameters.	Was P. Vigoureaux in the neighborhood of the crystal's resonant frequency?	P. Vigoureaux has derived the following values for the parameters in the neighborhood of the crystal's resonant frequency.
A high-voltage supply must be used to be able to change the coil currents rapidly.	Is the high-voltage supply able to change the currents?	A high-voltage supply must be used to permit the coil currents to be changed rapidly.

Original Example	Comments	Suggested Revision
Shell Chemical Corp. has dedicated here the world's first large-scale plant for making synthetic glycerine. . . . Often in critically short supply, Shell engineers have been at work on problems connected with the large-scale synthetic production of glycerine for many years. —*Christian Science Monitor*	It's wonderful to be a Shell engineer—they're in such demand.	[Better rewrite this sentence completely.]

14.5 Split Infinitive

You have probably been taught that the split infinitive is a particularly bad fault. You should try to avoid this construction, but not at the expense of (1) reducing clarity or (2) sounding forced and artificial.

Here is a perfectly clear sentence that contains a split infinitive.

A study must be included to properly integrate the computer with the other main components of the control system.

You might move the splitting word—*properly*—to any of several different places:

(1) A study must be included properly to integrate the computer . . .

Now *properly* might modify *included*. This revision must be rejected because it makes the sentence ambiguous.

(2) A study must be included to integrate properly the computer with the other main components of the control system.

This sounds strange and foreign, because it simply is not English idiom. It must be rejected.

(3) A study must be included to integrate the computer with the other main components of the control system properly.

Now *properly* is so far removed from *integrate* that it seems to hang by itself, unattached.

> (4) A study must be included to integrate the computer properly with the other main components of the control system.

This is the best of the four possible revisions, but it still lacks the clarity and the vigor of the original with the split infinitive.

Here is another clear sentence that contains a split infinitive:

> Consumption is expected to more than double by 1975.

The words in this sentence cannot go in any other order and still say the same thing. To avoid this split infinitive—if you must—you will have to rewrite the sentence entirely.

Nowadays most authorities take a moderate view of the split infinitive. You should not hesitate to use it when it is the clearest, most natural way of expressing your meaning.

But you can often avoid the split infinitive with no difficulty. Generally, if you can move the splitting word toward the end of the sentence without beclouding your meaning, the revision will be a successful one. But if you have to move the splitting word toward the beginning of the sentence, the result is likely to sound artificial and perhaps ambiguous, as in the following example.

Original Example	Suggested Revision
This course should help the engineer more quickly and effectively to handle a number of perplexing situations than he will if it is left to his own judgment and experience to work them out.	This course should help the engineer to handle a number of perplexing situations more quickly and effectively than he will if it is left to his own judgment and experience to work them out.

Here are several split infinitives susceptible of easy repair:

It is possible to so construct such an amplifier that its behavior is almost independent of frequency over a wide range.	It is possible to construct such an amplifier so that its behavior is almost independent of frequency over a wide range.

But notice the artificial, stilted sound of

> It is possible so to construct such an amplifier . . .

An adjustment is provided to intermittently check the calibration of the gauge.	An adjustment is provided to check the calibration of the gauge intermittently.

Notice the ambiguity of

An adjustment is provided intermittently to check the calibration of the gauge.

Original Example	Suggested Revision
. . . to more easily visualize just what happens to the money that is invested.	. . . to visualize more easily just what happens to the money that is invested.
. . . to sketchily mention all of the minute procedures . . .	. . . to mention sketchily all of the minute procedures . . .

Finally, remember that the split infinitive is specifically the separation of a verb from the auxiliary *to*. Verbs appear also with other auxiliaries, from which you may separate them with no qualms at all, so long as you do not separate them too far. For instance, *to always come* is a split infinitive; *have always come, do always come, will always come* are not. Similarly, *to forever be going* is a split infinitive; *to be forever going* is not.

14.6 Tense

You have probably been warned never to switch tenses in the middle of the stream. In general this is good advice; certainly you should not switch tenses needlessly.

But logic and meaning sometimes require two tenses in the same sentence. This situation often arises in technical writing in the description of an event that took place in the past but that depended on some principle or fact or relationship that continues to hold in the present. Thus we may better modify the rule and say: *Be sure that every change of tense carries some significance.*

For instance, in order to maintain consistency of tenses you might write:

The balloon rose because hydrogen was less dense than air.

This sentence implies that hydrogen used to be less dense than air, but that it isn't any more. That is manifestly absurd. To make your meaning clear you must mix tenses within the sentence:

The balloon rose because hydrogen is less dense than air.

But complications arise when tenses are shifted meaninglessly. Here are some examples:

Original Example	Suggested Revision
Tests *have shown* that the heat contents of various gasolines *differ* by about 3 percent in Btu per pound. But when the same fuels *were* evaluated in terms of Btu per gallon, the differences *were* as high as 15 percent.	Tests *have shown* that the heat contents of various gasolines *differ* by about 3 percent in Btu per pound. But when the same fuels *are* evaluated in terms of Btu per gallon, the differences *are* as high as 15 percent.

The revised version still contains two different tenses; the switch does carry some meaning.

The first charge breaks part of the material and forms a weak point. The following charges expend more of their energy in the direction of this weak point than they would have if they had been fired at the same time as the first charge.	The first charge breaks part of the material and forms a weak point. The following charges expend more of their energy in the direction of this weak point than they would if they were fired at the same time as the first charge.

14.7 Parallelism

Logic and orderliness demand parallel grammatical constructions for parallel ideas. More important, parallel constructions will make your meaning clearer, because a changed (or nonparallel) construction hints to the reader that the subject has been changed too.

Original Example	Suggested Revision
In compression the pieces broke off in a plane 45 degrees to the long axis. The tensile fracture was perpendicular to the long axis.	In compression the pieces fractured in a plane 45 degrees to the long axis. In tension they fractured perpendicular to the long axis.

In the original version the difference between the fractures is obscured by the difference between the sentences. In the next two examples, faulty parallelism leads to real momentary confusion, because the parallel ideas seem to merge rather than to stand separately.

If the meter under test is fast, the dial reading will be less than 1.0; and more than 1.0 if it is slow.	If the meter under test is fast, the dial reading will be less than 1.0; if it is slow, the dial reading will be more than 1.0.
Titles of articles or chapters in printed matter should be in italics and underlined when typed.	Titles of articles or chapters in printed matter should be in italics; in typed matter they should be underlined.

Executives in the Sales Division should be *marketing-conscious* [adjective] rather than *good production men* [noun].

Executives in the Sales Division should be *salesmen* rather than *production men.*

The customer would *ask* for a certain brand rather than *asking* for recommendations.

The customer would *ask* for a certain brand rather than *ask* for recommendations.

The testing of these meters involves a comparison of the speed of the meter disc under test with the disc speed of a secondary meter standard.

The testing of these meters involves a comparison of the disc speed of the meter under test with the disc speed of a secondary meter standard.

He will also learn the correct pronunciation and that there are two ways of spelling the word.

He will also learn the correct pronunciation, and he will find that there are two ways of spelling the word.

14.7.1 Lists

Faulty parallelism is particularly obvious and particularly annoying in any kind of list or enumeration.

Original Example	Suggested Revision
The shielding for the system is provided by the *use* of coaxial cable to connect sensing elements, *insertion* of r-f chokes in the power supply, and *enclosing* the tank circuits in shielded cans.	The shielding for the system is provided by the *use* of coaxial cable to connect sensing elements, *insertion* of r-f chokes in the power supply, and *enclosure* of the tank circuits in shielded cans.
1. Nonequilibrium conditions. 2. Sampling. 3. Excessive heat. 4. Other elements present may have interfered.	1. Nonequilibrium conditions. 2. Sampling. 3. Excessive heat. 4. Possible interference by other elements present.
A knowledge of the carburetor air temperature is needed *for adjustments* of throttle position and *to warn* of icing conditions.	A knowledge of the carburetor air temperature is needed *for adjustments* of throttle position and *for warning* of icing conditions.
Smith pointed out *how* Jones opposed every innovation, *how* he encouraged the men to slow down, *that* he never took the initiative, and *that* he could not keep the machines running.	Smith pointed out *that* Jones opposed every innovation, *that* he encouraged the men to slow down, *that* he never took the initiative, and *that* he could not keep the machines running.
The assumptions made are: (1) the accuracy of the measuring means is greater than the accuracy of the instrument being measured; (2) the noise level and drift are less than the inaccuracy of linearity; and (3) *that* the points of maximum deviation from the straight line are known.	Omit *that.*

14.7.2 Bastard Enumeration

You are familiar with the series form, or enumeration, *a, b, and c,* in which the letters stand for elements of almost any grammatical form—words, phrases, clauses, or even sentences. (For the punctuation of the series see Sec. 15.2.4.) As shown in Sec. 14.7.1, all of the elements in any one series must be of the same grammatical form.

Further, remember that *any external operator that operates on more than one element of a series operates automatically on* all *the elements of the series.* Disregard of this rule produces a special form of non-parallel construction that Fowler calls the *bastard enumeration* (*Modern English Usage*). The bastard enumeration looks like a legitimate enumeration but isn't one. It is a subtle fault that plagues many good writers. Because it is an offense against logic and clarity, you should avoid it.

Consider this sentence:

> Adapters are made in various sizes, shapes, weights, and with any number of leads.

The elements of this enumeration are (*a*) sizes, (*b*) shapes, (*c*) weights, and (*d*) with any number of leads. The words *in various* obviously operate on *a, b,* and *c;* they therefore operate also on *d.* The result is . . . *in various with any number of leads.*

The cure for this error is often the insertion of another *and,* which separates the bastard enumeration into two parts, one of which is a true enumeration:

> Adapters are made in various sizes, shapes, *and* weights, and with any number of leads.

Now *with any number of leads* is not an element of the series; and *in various* operates only on *sizes, shapes,* and *weights.*

This bastard enumeration may be corrected in another way:

> Adapters are made in various sizes, in various shapes, in various weights, and with any number of leads.

Now *in various* is not an external operator; it is repeated within each of the first three elements of the enumeration and so does not have any connection with the fourth.

Here are some other examples of the bastard enumeration:

Original Example	Comments	Suggested Revision
When maintained at the appropriate pH, osmotic pressure, and in the presence of certain salts . . .	*Maintained at* operates on *appropriate pH* and *osmotic pressure;* therefore also on *in the presence of certain salts.*	When maintained at the appropriate pH *and* osmotic pressure, and in the presence of certain salts . . .
The tape equipment is undergoing test to determine operating characteristics, relay timing, power requirements, fusing, and to suppress undesirable transients.	Since *to suppress undesirable transients* seems to be a member of the series, *to determine* operates on it.	The tape equipment is undergoing tests to determine operating characteristics, relay timing, power requirements, *and* fusing, *as well as* to suppress undesirable transients.
The thiomorpholide was extracted with ether, washed with 10-percent sodium carbonate, 10-percent hydrochloric acid, and with water.	1. *Extracted with ether* is fused into the series that starts with *washed with.* 2. *Washed with* operates on *10-percent sodium carbonate* and *10-percent hydrochloric acid,* and therefore also on *with water.*	The thiomorpholide was extracted with ether *and* washed with 10-percent sodium carbonate, 10-percent hydrochloric acid, and water.
March 29, 30, 31, and April 1.		March 29, 30, and 31 and April 1.

14.8 Preposition at End of Sentence

At some time during your schooling you may have been taught that no sentence should end with a preposition. This view is now held only by pedants. Good present-day writers end sentences with prepositions whenever that is the natural word order. The sentence that has been revised to avoid a preposition at the end is often stilted or awkward.

Rejoice: here is one "rule" that you can just forget about.

14.9 Number with Collectives

A noun that denotes a whole made up of a number of similar parts is called a collective. Common examples are: pair, set, group, majority, 30 inches, two million dollars. Notice that some of these words are singular in form, others plural.

A collective may take either a singular verb or a plural verb, depending upon its sense. When it refers to the whole group as a unit, the collective takes a singular verb. When it refers to the separate entities that go to make up the group, the collective takes a plural verb. The number of the pronoun that stands for a collective must of course agree with the number of the verb.

This rule is commonly overlooked. Many writers stick slavishly to singular verbs with all collectives that are singular in form and to plural verbs with all collectives that are plural in form. You can help your reader by making the number of the verb fit the sense of the collective rather than its form.

14.9.1 Apparently Plural Words

Would you say "Two million dollars are a lot of money"? No, you would say "Two million dollars *is* a lot of money." You are referring not to the separate dollars, but to the whole sum of money. Yet technical writers often becloud their meaning by using plural verbs in this construction:

Original Example	Suggested Revision
Ten grams of the isotope *were* collected.	Ten grams of the isotope *was* collected.
To 200 grams of sodium *were* added 1.5 kilograms of crushed ice.	To 200 grams of sodium *was* added 1.5 kilograms of crushed ice.
In the forward hold there *are* 16 inches of water. *It* [!] must be pumped out.	In the forward hold there *is* 16 inches of water. *It* must be pumped out.

The writers of these examples were referring not to separate grams and kilograms and inches, but to a quantity of isotope and a quantity of ice and a quantity of water measured in grams and kilograms and inches. The singular verbs make sense; the plural verbs do not.

On the other hand you would, of course, say "A million pennies *were* scattered around the vault."

14.9.2 Apparently Singular Words

You have probably heard an exclamation like "A pair of jacks *is* the highest hand I've seen for an hour." The unlucky gamester is referring not to the separate jacks, but to the pair as a unit. The singular verb makes sense. But now consider this statement:

> A pair of hawks was taking turns feeding the young birds.

How can a single entity (as implied by the singular verb) take turns? A clearer and more logical statement is:

> A pair of hawks were taking turns feeding the young birds.

The singular verb with a collective that is plural in sense though singular in form can produce a construction that is both illogical and inconsistent, as in the following example.

Original Example	Suggested Revision
In beta-decay some of the neutrons already in the nucleus are changed to protons, and an equal number of electrons *is* emitted by the nucleus.	In beta-decay some of the neutrons already in the nucleus are changed to protons, and an equal number of electrons *are* omitted by the nucleus.

Here are some other examples of plural verbs (and pronouns) used logically with collectives that are plural in sense though singular in form:

> The *majority were* between 1.5 and 2.5 millimeters long; *they* moved constantly and randomly. The *rest were* mostly smaller; *they were* also less active.

> *A number* of ill-concealed snickers *were* heard in the back of the lecture hall.

14.9.3 Data

The word *data* used to be defined only as *plural of datum*. It meant *facts* or *figures*. To use it with a singular verb was considered highly improper.

Over a comparatively short span of years *data* has come to mean also *information*. In this sense it is logically singular. Thus *data* is a collective, and the number of its verb may be either singular or plural, depending upon whether it means *a body of information* or a lot of *separate figures*.

Some authorities of the old school still insist that *data* must never appear with a singular verb (or pronoun). But unless your boss objects, you should probably use *data* as singular or plural according to its meaning.

In the first example below, the singular would not make sense. In the second, the plural would sound very stilted.

> The data *were* plotted point by point. Some of *them were* found to be grossly in error.

> The data developed by the Senate investigators *is* going to be published in full next year. *It* should be helpful to anyone working in the field of criminology.

14.10 Spelling

There is little inherent virtue in spelling correctly. But spelling errors, like some other apparently trivial errors, have much the same effect as saying *ain't*: they make the reader wonder whether the writer is educated; whether, indeed, he knows what he is talking about. You owe it to yourself to spell correctly.

Whenever you have a serious writing job to do, be sure to keep a dictionary close by and consult it freely. (For recommended dictionaries see Sec. 13.2.5.)

If you find that you are inclined to make spelling errors, keep a list of the words you have spelled wrong and look at it from time to time. If you are constitutionally unable to learn spelling (we have met a few people who claim to be), the least you can do is to have some more capable friend go over everything you write before you submit it to the people who count.

Here are some principles of spelling that most people find to be of considerable help.

(1) A final consonant is doubled before an ending that begins with a vowel when the word to be obtained is accented on the final syllable of the root word.

prefer	preferred
prefer	preference
occur	occurrence

(2) When words contain *ei* or *ie*, *i* usually comes before the *e*, except when the combination comes after *c*.

believe	retrieve	receive

(3) Some poor spelling results from careless pronunciation. If, in conversation, you leave off syllables or add them where they don't belong, you may spell these words as given in the *wrong* column.

Wrong	Right
accidently	accidentally
athelete	athlete
preform	perform
perserverance	perseverance

(4) We should add a note here on *preferred* spelling. Some of the words we use, particularly those we use in common with the English, have gone through a process of *Americanization*. In most technical writing, the American version is preferred. When you know that two versions exist but you don't know which is preferred, consult your dictionary.

Here are some examples of words that have changed their spelling:

American	English
acknowledgment	acknowledgement
judgment	judgement
maneuver	manoeuvre
practice (verb)	practise
theater	theatre

(5) Three pairs of words whose members are pronounced alike but spelled differently cause a lot of spelling errors in technical writing. These words are distinguished below (only the meanings that are commonly confused are given).

a. { Principle: Noun = basis, fundamental truth, basic law.
{ Principal: Adjective = chief, foremost.

b. { Effect: { Noun = result produced.
{   { Verb = bring about, accomplish.
{ Affect: Verb = influence; have an *effect* on.

c. { Foreword: Noun = preface (front *word*).
{ Forward: Adjective, adverb = toward the front (front *direction*).

The technical writer should be on his guard about some words that will appear frequently in his writing:

accommodation	judgment	personnel
acknowledgment	laboratory	precede
analogous	maintenance	proceed
carburetor	occurred	procedure
cylinder	occurrence	propeller
exceed	questionnaire	schedule
guarantee	pamphlet	superintendent

15. WRITING: PUNCTUATION

15.1 A Help to Your Reader

Proper punctuation performs an indispensable function: it helps to make the writer's meaning precise and clear; and it eases the reader's task. Conversely, slipshod punctuation can actually alter meaning; at the very least it puts the reader (perhaps many readers) to a lot of unnecessary trouble.

Possibly because of the insignificant physical aspect of punctuation marks, some people consider the whole subject trivial and beneath their notice. Others are careless about punctuation on the plea that they like the "open style" or the smooth-flowing effect associated with a general absence of punctuation.

This attitude may be appropriate for some kinds of writing; but remember that the primary aim of technical reporting is to transmit information accurately and efficiently. Since punctuation can play an important part in this process, you should take the trouble to punctuate your technical writing fairly rigorously. If you don't like the looks or the effect of a lot of commas, the way to get rid of them is not to omit clarifying punctuation, but to construct your sentences so that little punctuation is needed.

Most technical students have had elementary training in composition that was directed to all the students in a high school class or a college freshman class without regard to their future specialization.   Furthermore, the teachers of these classes have probably had a literary rather than a technical background.   Consequently some of the principles propounded in *Technical Reporting* may differ from those you have been taught before.   Since this book is designed for the technical writer, you will probably do well to heed its advice whenever your primary aim is precision and clarity rather than literary effect.

You can learn to do a reasonably good job of punctuating without memorizing a large number of formal rules.   The remainder of this chapter presents some general principles and some rules of thumb that should help you.   It stresses only a few highly important formal rules that are commonly overlooked.   If you need further information on punctuation, consult a composition handbook (see Sec. 14.1) or look up the excellent articles on punctuation in the back of *Webster's Collegiate Dictionary* and the front of *The American College Dictionary*.

15.2 The Comma

15.2.1 General Function of the Comma

The comma is a separator, or pause-indicator.   It separates words or parts of sentences that would otherwise run together.   It is the lightest member of the series that consists of the period, the semicolon, and the comma.   It tells the reader those things that a speaker indicates to his listeners by pausing or dropping his voice.

This suggests a rule of thumb for the use of the comma.   *Whenever you wonder whether to insert a comma, read your sentence aloud, with exaggerated expression.   Generally speaking, where the tone of your voice changes or where you pause momentarily, a comma belongs.*

Read these two sentences aloud, slowly:

> It is therefore important for every engineer to be a man of honor.
> It is, therefore, important for every engineer to be a man of honor.

Notice that you go straight through the first sentence without pause. But in the second sentence you pause before and after *therefore;* you say *therefore* in a slightly subdued tone; and you give a little stress to *is.*

There is no question here of "correct" punctuation; both sentences are correctly punctuated. The commas in the second sentence simply change the emphasis. Often, of course, commas play a much more vital role: by indicating separations, they actually control meaning.

You can usually decide whether to use a comma on the basis of this simple voice-drop test. But the functions of the comma described in Secs. 15.2.2–15.2.8 are so important (and so often overlooked) that you should learn to recognize them and the rules that govern them. *The rules in Secs. 15.2.2, 15.2.3, and 15.2.4 are particularly important; you should probably follow them formally and rigorously.* Notice, however, that the voice-drop criterion fits in with these rules, too.

15.2.2 The Comma in Compound Sentences

The compound sentence is usually a sentence made up of two independent clauses (i.e., independent sentences) joined by a coordinating conjunction such as *and, or, but,* or *for.* Most grammar books say to put a comma before the conjunction unless the clauses are very short. This advice seems to be taken by most people to mean that the comma can usually be omitted.

If you want to be sure that you will never confuse your reader, even temporarily, you must get in the habit of using a comma in this construction practically always. The following examples illustrate the momentary misunderstanding that sometimes occurs when the comma is omitted.

Original Example	Confusing Passage	Suggested Revision
Throughout the islands move numerous small craft and larger vessels make regular calls at the larger ports.	. . . move numerous small craft and larger vessels . . .	Throughout the islands move numerous small craft, and larger vessels make regular calls at the larger ports.
A few modifications were made on the operation matrix drivers and the control-pulse output units will be modified.	. . . modifications were made on the operation matrix drivers and the control-pulse output units . . .	A few modifications were made on the operation matrix drivers, and the control-pulse output units will be modified.
Your schedules must be revised or corrected versions will not be ready for the next report.	. . . schedules must be revised or corrected . . .	Your schedules must be revised, or corrected versions will not be ready for the next report.

Original Example	Confusing Passage	Suggested Revision
When a code is found, the control causes it to be set up in the relay register associated with the reader and the contents of the two relay registers are then checked for coincidence.	. . . associated with the reader and the contents of the two relay registers . . .	When a code is found, the control causes it to be set up in the relay register associated with the reader, and the contents of the two relay registers are then checked for coincidence.
Air brakes can give very rapid decelerations and the ability to reduce speed abruptly could be helpful in an approach system.	. . . give very rapid decelerations and the ability to reduce speed abruptly . . .	Air brakes can give very rapid decelerations, and the ability to reduce speed abruptly could be helpful in an approach system.

The insertion of a comma before the conjunction clarifies every one of these sentences. But most of them could be further improved by more extensive revisions, particularly by being changed from compound sentences to complex sentences, with one of the clauses subordinated (see Sec. 13.12). For instance, the third example would be more meaningful if it read:

> Unless your schedules are revised, correct versions will not be ready for the next report.

15.2.3 The Comma around Nonrestrictive Modifiers

The restrictive modifier pins down its object to a certain one (or certain ones) from a larger class:

> Men seldom make passes at girls *who wear glasses.*
> —Dorothy Parker

We are not talking about girls in general; just that restricted group *who wear glasses.* The restrictive (or defining) modifier is essential to the meaning of the statement; *it is never set off by commas.*

The nonrestrictive modifier, on the other hand, simply makes a comment about its object without limiting our choice:

> Grammar, *which is a dull subject,* is important.

Are we limiting ourselves to that part of grammar which is a dull subject? No; all grammar is dull; we are simply adding this comment. The nonrestrictive modifier is not essential to the meaning of a statement; *it should always be set off in commas.*

If you have difficulty in deciding whether a modifier is restrictive or nonrestrictive, try crossing it out. If what remains is still a sensible statement, the modifier is nonessential, or nonrestrictive. For instance,

> Grammar . . . is important.

is a perfectly sensible statement even if you don't agree with it. The modifier *which is a dull subject* should therefore be set off in commas. On the other hand, if what remains is no longer a sensible statement, the modifier is essential, or restrictive. For instance,

> *Men seldom make passes at girls. . . .*

is manifestly absurd. The modifier *who wear glasses* should not be set off by a comma.

The modifiers in the two examples above are both relative clauses, because it is the punctuation of relative-clause modifiers that seems to cause most of the difficulty. But the same rules apply to other kinds of modifiers, as in the following examples:

> Reports *written by engineers for engineers* may contain algebraic expressions. (Restrictive.)
> Reports, *written or oral,* should be as clear and as short as possible. (Nonrestrictive.)

Technical writers occasionally make the mistake of putting commas around restrictive modifiers, particularly long ones. Much more often, though, they omit the commas from nonrestrictive modifiers, a usage for which they can find ample precedent in the newspapers.

Some writers take the attitude that they will put commas around nonrestrictive modifiers whenever confusion would result without them. But unless you consistently put commas around *every* nonrestrictive modifier, you will sometimes leave your readers in doubt.

Suppose you are *not* rigorous about this rule. In a report you write:

> This drawing shows the end sections *which differ from the middle sections.*

Your reader wonders whether you purposely omitted a comma after *end sections.* If you did, *which differ from the middle sections* is restrictive, and you are talking about just those end sections which differ from the middle sections. But perhaps all the end sections are alike, and you are simply commenting that they differ from the middle sections. You thought a comma after *end sections* unnecessary. How is your reader to know which you intended? As a matter of fact, the writer of that sentence simply neglected to put a comma after *end sections,* where it was required by his meaning.

Here are two more examples that are ambiguous from a writer who is not rigorous about punctuating nonrestrictive modifiers:

> The filter acts as a diffusing screen for the air *which enters the top of the chamber.*
> This cell energizes the thyratron tube *which draws current through the coils.*

Again, the writers of these sentences were slipshod, and each of the relative clauses should have been preceded by a comma. You should get into the habit of putting commas around every nonrestrictive modifier, no matter how simple and obvious it may be.

15.2.4 The Comma in Series

Teaching differs on the punctuation of the series, or enumeration, of the form *a, b, and c.* Some schools say that the comma preceding the conjunction should be omitted; others that it should be omitted except where confusion would result; and still others that it should always be used. *Unless you put a comma before the conjunction in every series, you will sometimes confuse your readers.*

Suppose you write:

> Electric lenses were developed by Davisson and Calbrick, Knoll and Ruska and Bruche.

This is evidently meant to be a three-member series, *a, b,* and *c.* The first member, *a,* is obviously Davisson and Calbrick; but does Ruska belong with Knoll or with Bruche? As the sentence now stands, there is no clue.

Suppose you belong to the school that says the comma should go into this construction when confusion would result without it. Then you would write:

> . . . Davisson and Calbrick, Knoll and Ruska, and Bruche.

Remember, your reader has observed that you often omit the last comma in a series. When he comes to *Knoll and Ruska,* he thinks *momentarily* that the three members of the series are (*a*) Davisson and Calbrick, (*b*)

Knoll, and (c) Ruska. When he gets to *and Bruche,* he sees that Ruska goes with Knoll as the *b* member of the series, and he understands you completely.

On the other hand, if he has observed that you never omit that last comma, he knows immediately that Ruska is not the last member of a series, and he is not misled even momentarily.

Now consider this passage:

> If we have subdivisions of *X, Y* and *Z,* whose values are known. . . .

Do we have three subdivisions—(1) of *X,* (2) of *Y,* and (3) of *Z?* Or do we have two subdivisions of *X* that we are calling respectively *Y* and *Z?* If this passage comes from a writer who consistently puts a comma before the conjunction in a series, we know that the three letters are not members of a series, and that *Y* and *Z* are subdivisions of *X.* But from a writer who is not consistent, how are we to tell? As a matter of fact, the man who wrote that passage intended to speak of subdivisions of *X, Y,* and *Z.*

Here is a similar sentence:

> A sampling device is made up of two cascaded components, a sampling switch and a cascaded holding device.

From a nonrigorous punctuator, this sentence might be momentarily interpreted in either of two ways: (1) a sampling device is made up of three elements—(a) two cascaded components, (b) a sampling switch, and (c) a cascaded holding device; or, (2) a sampling device is made up of two cascaded components—namely, a sampling switch and a cascaded holding device. On the other hand, if this passage had come from a rigorous punctuator, we would know at once that no series was intended, and that the words *a sampling switch and a cascaded holding device* are simply further explanation of *two cascaded components.* (To remove all doubt, use a dash instead of a comma after *components;* see Sec. 15.5.)

To be on the safe side, get in the habit of putting a comma before the conjunction of *every* series.

15.2.5 The Comma with Adjectives in Series

Two or more adjectives preceding the noun they modify constitute a special kind of series. If these adjectives modify the noun separately and independently, they should be separated from each other by commas. On the other hand, if the earlier adjectives modify not only the noun but also the succeeding adjectives, they should not be separated by commas. This rule can be expressed algebraically. Let b, c, d be adjectives; x, a noun.

$$(b + c + d)x\text{—Commas to separate } b, c, d.$$
$$b\{c\,[d(x)]\}\text{—No commas.}$$

For example you would write

a big, ungainly freshman.

Big and *ungainly* operate separately on *freshman*.

On the other hand, you would write

a big black dog.

Big modifies the whole concept of *black dog*.

Here is a rule of thumb to determine when adjectives in series should be separated by commas: Try putting the word *and* at each place where you think a comma might belong. If the passage still sounds sensible, use the comma; if it doesn't, omit the comma. If you are in doubt, omit the comma.

Application of this test to the examples above produces

a big and ungainly freshman,

which is sensible, and

a big and black dog,

which is silly.

Here are several other examples of adjectives in series. You can confirm the usage of commas by trying the *and* test.

Commas Indicated	Commas Not Indicated
A big, powerful, handsome motor	A wound-rotor alternating-current repulsion-induction motor
A badly worn, obsolete engine	A 4-cycle gasoline engine
A hasty, careless, inaccurate statement	A hasty rearward flight

For a discussion of the *compound adjective*, which is a combination of words rather than a succession of separate words, see Sec.15 .7.2.

15.2.6 The Comma after Introductory Elements

Section 15.2.1 points out that the comma is used to separate words or parts of sentences that would otherwise run together. The introductory phrase or clause (an adverbial phrase or relative clause that comes before the main clause) often seems to run on into the rest of the sentence, at least momentarily. You can avoid this source of confusion by putting a comma after every introductory phrase or clause (unless it is very short and the break between it and the main clause is obvious).

Original Example	Confusing Passage	Suggested Revision
At the instant of starting the motor draws more than 400 amperes.	. . . starting the motor . . .	At the instant of starting, the motor draws more than 400 amperes.
When propagation time and switching time are allowed for the hypothetical system would probably require a pulse-repetition frequency of 20 kilocycles.	. . . allowed for the hypothetical system . . .	When propagation time and switching time are allowed for, the hypothetical system would probably require a pulse-repetition frequency of 20 kilocycles.
When the bulb is exposed to temperatures different from that of the medium in which the stem is placed a severe gradient exists across the bulb.		When the bulb is exposed to temperatures different from that of the medium in which the stem is placed, a severe gradient exists across the bulb.
As the rate of current change increases the slope of the portions representing the drops will increase.	. . . increases the slope . . .	As the rate of current change increases, the slope of the portions representing the drops will increase.
Whenever the computer is operating the control element is generating a succession of pulses.	. . . computer is operating the control element . . .	Whenever the computer is operating, the control element is generating a succession of pulses.

Several of these examples would be further improved by more extensive revision. The commas at least make them clear.

15.2.7 Second Comma of Parenthetical Pair

The single comma is the lightest in the series of pause-indicators that consists of the period, the semicolon, and the comma. Similarly, the *pair* of commas is the lightest in the series of parentheses that consists of the pair of curves (or parentheses; see Sec. 15.6), the pair of dashes (see Sec. 15.5), and the pair of commas.

Most writers often use the pair of commas as a light parenthesis, although they may not think of the usage in these terms. A common fault is the omission of the second comma of a parenthetical pair. This confuses the reader, because he is momentarily uncertain where the parenthetical remark ends and the main stream resumes. He has had one pause indicated; he feels the need for a second, but he does not find it.

Original Example	Suggested Revision
The train passes the plants of several large industrial shippers, such as the Davison Chemical Co. and the American Oil Co. which fill many cars every day.	The train passes the plants of several large industrial shippers, such as the Davison Chemical Co. and the American Oil Co., which fill many cars every day. (Or omit *both* commas.)
The distance between Baltimore, Md. and Washington, D. C. is about 40 miles.	The distance between Baltimore, Md., and Washington, D. C., is about 40 miles.
The agreement ran from Jan. 1, 1950 to Dec. 31, 1952.	The agreement ran from Jan. 1, 1950, to Dec. 31, 1952.
Argentina, the second largest nation in South America with an area of over a million square miles, is located in the southeastern part of the continent.	Argentina, the second largest nation in South America, with an area of over a million square miles, is located in the southeastern part of the continent.

15.2.8 The Comma between Closely Related Parts

Since the comma is a separator, it should *not* go between elements that are very closely related. In particular, a comma should not separate a verb from its subject, its object, or its complement. The temptation to put a comma between subject and verb is strongest with a long subject that seems to call for a breather. A better solution is to rewrite the sentence or shorten the subject.

Original Example	Suggested Revision
That he runs from danger, is an important indicator of a man's character.	That he runs from danger is an important indicator of a man's character.

Notice, however, that a *pair* of commas between verb and subject is all right, because the second comma of the pair shows that the inter-ruption is over and the main stream has been rejoined.

The brave man, although afraid, does not run from danger.

15.3 The Semicolon

It is possible to write grammatically and clearly without ever using a semicolon. But the semicolon, as an intermediate-weight separator, can often help you express meaning clearly. The semicolon is most likely to be useful in three constructions:

15.3.1 The Semicolon with "Heavy" Connective Words

When certain so-called "heavy" or "uncommon" connective words join two independent clauses, the rules call for a stop heavier than a comma preceding them. A semicolon is suitable. Chief among this group of words are *however, therefore, nevertheless, moreover, otherwise, hence, also, thus,* and *yet.*

If you put a comma before any of these words when it is being used as a connective, you are guilty of a sin known as the *comma splice.* This fault leads to only very momentary confusion, but it is a mark of the unpracticed writer; therefore you should avoid it in order to main-tain your reputation.

Original Example	Suggested Revision
The engine was badly damaged, never-theless, the plane still flew.	The engine was badly damaged; never-theless, the plane still flew.
The circuit is clearly shown, therefore, I shall not describe it in detail.	The circuit is clearly shown; therefore, I shall not describe it in detail.
The angle is not correct, however, it ap-proximates the required deviation.	The angle is not correct; however, it approximates the required deviation.

(Any of these semicolons could be replaced by a period.)

Notice that the rule is corroborated by the voice-drop test: the break before these connective words is slightly greater than the one after them.

The words of this group are often used not as connectives *between* independent clauses but as adverbs *within* clauses. In this construction they may be enclosed in a pair of parenthetical commas.

The engine was badly damaged.   The plane, nevertheless, still flew.

The angle is not correct.   It does, however, approximate the required deviation.

15.3.2 The Semicolon between Closely Related Independent Clauses

The close logical relationship between two independent clauses (sentences) without any connective word can be indicated by a semicolon.

I shall be out of town Tuesday; you may come to see me Wednesday.

This use of the semicolon can be helpful in avoiding a monotonous succession of short declarative sentences (Sec. 13.6).

Original Example	Suggested Revision
The gas inlet is a rectangular pipe entering tangential to the body of the cyclone. The gas outlet is an inner concentric cylinder extending down into the body of the cyclone. The outlet for deposited dust is at the bottom of the cone.	The gas inlet is a rectangular pipe entering tangential to the body of the cyclone; the gas outlet is an inner concentric cylinder extending down into the body. The outlet for deposited dust is at the bottom of the cone.

But if you use a comma to separate two independent clauses without any connective word, you will again be guilty of a comma splice.   Don't do it.

Original Example	Suggested Revision
The transistor eliminates the problem of heating, it consumes only about a millionth the power of an equivalent vacuum tube.	The transistor eliminates the problem of heating, *because* it consumes only about a millionth the power of an equivalent vacuum tube.

or:

The transistor eliminates the problem of heating; it consumes only about a millionth the power of an equivalent vacuum tube.

or:

The transistor eliminates the problem of heating.   It consumes only about a millionth the power of an equivalent vacuum tube.

15.3.3 The Semicolon instead of Commas

Sentence elements that are normally separated by commas may themselves contain internal commas. It is then sometimes difficult to distinguish between the internal commas and the external commas that are supposed to separate the elements. Whenever commas are liable to become confused in this way, semicolons may be substituted at your discretion for the external, or heavier, commas.

Original Example	Suggested Revision
Such a program could have been initiated through written discussions in the leading farm journals, missionary salesmen to discuss the use, applications, and benefits of the fertilizer at the local Grange or other similar organizational meetings, and experiments conducted by the various large universities which have agricultural schools.	Such a program could have been initiated through written discussions in the leading farm journals; missionary salesmen to discuss the use, applications, and benefits of the fertilizer at the local Grange or other similar organizational meetings; and experiments conducted by the various large universities which have agricultural schools.
The output amplifier will consist of a phase inverter to drive the output pair of tubes, the output pair, with cathode resistors, to form a voltage proportional to load current, circuits which are the analogue of the deflection coils, an inverter to invert one of the analogue outputs, and a mixer to add the resulting two signals, whose sum will be compared with the input.	The output amplifier will consist of a phase inverter to drive the output pair of tubes; the output pair, with cathode resistors, to form a voltage proportional to load current; circuits which are the analogue of the deflection coils; an inverter to invert one of the analogue outputs; and a mixer to add the resulting two signals, whose sum will be compared with the input.

Of course either of these sentences might be further clarified by the addition of numbers for the items set off in semicolons, or perhaps by being broken up into several sentences.

Notice that in both revised sentences the conjunction *and* before the last member of the series is preceded by a semicolon (not a comma), in order to keep the punctuation parallel.

15.4 The Colon

15.4.1 General Function of the Colon

The colon was once a member of the series of pause-indicators that now consists of the period, the semicolon, and the comma. In modern technical writing the colon is a separate, highly specialized punctuation mark. Its function may be illustrated this way:

> Promise : fulfillment.

That is, the colon comes after a statement that promises more information; it separates the promise from the fulfillment. Because the colon is reserved for this special function, it acts as a signal. Whenever you see a colon (except in certain conventional uses; see Sec. 15.4.5), you can expect further information about the subject that has just been mentioned.

15.4.2 The Colon to Introduce a Formal List

The simplest and commonest promise-fulfillment function is the introduction of a formal list.

> These tubes were chosen for the circuits: 7AK7, 7AD7, 3E29, 6YG6, and 6SN7.

> This work has included the measurement of the following parameters: (1) charging-current distribution; (2) spot interaction; (3) spot stability; and (4) gate lengths and amplitudes.

> The requirements for a satisfactory voltmeter for this service are:
> 1. It must be accurate to ± 2 volts at full scale.
> 2. It must be insensitive to accelerations of 5 g.
> 3. It must be easily readable from 5 feet.

Because the colon is a further-information signal, you can usually omit the words *as follows*, or *the following*, from the introduction to a list. The colon itself leads the reader to expect more to follow.

15.4.3 The Colon to Introduce a Formal Quotation

The colon is used to introduce a formal quotation.

> The instruction manual has this to say: "With the left foot depress the clutch pedal. Move the gear-shift lever up and then toward yourself. With the right foot depress the accelerator pedal slightly. Then slowly release the clutch pedal."

15.4.4 The Colon to Introduce Further Explanation

In a less common construction, the colon introduces a statement that supplies *further explanation* of the statement that precedes it.

Load conditions in the test must duplicate actual operating conditions: first, the capacitance of the ignition harness must be 200 micromicrofarads; second, the shunt resistance of the spark gap must be kept to a minimum.

The damper control has a dual function: to maintain the proper proportion of cold air and heated air by regulating the mixing damper, and to control the velocity of the mixed air by regulating the outlet damper.

15.4.5 The Colon in Conventional Constructions

In addition, the colon is used in certain well-known conventional constructions, among them:

Between hours and minutes in an expression of time (7:28 A.M.)

After the greeting in a formal business letter (Gentlemen:)

Between various items in bibliographical entries (see Sec. 16.5.1)

15.5 The Dash

15.5.1 General Function of the Dash

The dash—another specialized punctuation mark—in general announces a discontinuity. (Do not confuse the dash with the hyphen, which is physically shorter and which serves an entirely different purpose; see Sec. 15.7.) As a signal of interruption, the dash is a useful but not essential mark whose functions overlap those of other marks. The rest of Sec. 15.5 describes several specific uses of the dash. Of these the ones discussed in Secs. 15.5.2, 15.5.3, and 15.5.4 are appropriate in technical writing; the rest should usually be avoided.

15.5.2 The Dash Paired as a Parenthesis

A pair of dashes makes an intermediate-weight parenthesis (see Sec. 15.2.7). An example of this usage appears in the first sentence of Sec. 15.5.1; the parenthetical remark could have been set off in a pair of commas, but they would have provided rather inadequate pauses for the interruption, or discontinuity. Similarly, the parenthetical remark could be set off in a pair of curves (Sec. 15.6), but they would separate it a little too completely from *dash,* to which it is logically close. The pair of dashes in this sentence conveys a shade of meaning that would be hard to express otherwise.

If the second dash of a parenthetical pair comes at the end of the sentence, it is omitted.

15.5.3 The Dash to Introduce a List

The dash may be used to introduce a list, like an informal colon (but do not use both a dash and a colon together).

> Some of the chassis members contribute to both unsprung weight and sprung weight—the driveshaft, the torque tube, the independent-suspension links, and the springs themselves.

The dash is often used to avoid confusion in a series. Take this example:

> He had put up for sale three pieces of machinery—a lathe, an electric saw, and a drill.

Here the author intended that three objects should be noted, not six. A comma might have caused such confusion; on the other hand, a colon could have been used.

15.5.4 The Dash to Introduce Further Explanation

Again like an informal colon, the dash may be used to announce further explanation of the statement that precedes it.

> In automatic service the engine undergoes fluctuating loads—both its torque and its speed are constantly changing.

> Sometimes we want a simplified description—a description that even a layman can understand easily.

15.5.5 The Dash in Other Uses

In nontechnical writing the dash is legitimately used for a number of other specialized purposes, such as to provide a pause before an unexpected word or a supposedly witty remark. Even in the most informal writing these uses of the dash should be employed sparingly if they are to be effective. In technical writing they should not be employed at all.

Some inexperienced or lazy writers use a great many dashes indiscriminately in place of other punctuation marks. This practice is of course confusing to the reader.

15.6 The Parenthesis

The general function of the parenthesis (or curves) is so well understood that no discussion is needed here.

15.6.1 The Parenthesis and Other Punctuation

The parenthesis should not be preceded by a comma. If a comma is required after the sentence element that comes before the parenthetical remark, the comma should follow the parenthetical remark. This rule is sensible, because the parenthetical remark is usually logically connected to what has gone before it. For example:

> Although the engineer was thoroughly familiar with the crossing (he had made this run daily for three years), he failed to slow down in time.

Notice that if the parenthetical remark were removed, the comma would come after *crossing*.

When a parenthetical remark is included as part of a sentence (even at the end of the sentence), the period goes outside the second curve, and the parenthetical remark does not begin with a capital, even though it is a complete sentence (see example above). When a whole sentence stands alone in parenthesis, the period goes inside the second curve, and the sentence begins with a capital. (This might be a good place to point out that the overuse of parentheses is often a sign of incomplete organization.)

15.6.2 The Parenthesis around Equation Numbers

Parentheses are customarily used around the numerals that distinguish items in an enumeration; for examples, see Secs. 15.2.4 and 15.4.2.

A special case of this usage is the numbering of equations. In any treatise or derivation that contains more than just a few equations, it is customary to number the equations serially. Each equation number is enclosed in parentheses and is usually placed at the right-hand margin opposite the equation.

This use of parentheses is logical and convenient. But many writers carry the parentheses over into their references to the equation numbers:

> Values of these parameters may be obtained by making the proper substitutions in Equations (11), (13), and (17).

In this construction the parentheses are separating the inseparable. The name of a certain equation is Equation 11, and there is no more reason to put *11* in parentheses than *Equation*. Whenever you refer to an equation (or other numbered item) by number, omit the parentheses even though they appear in the actual enumeration.

. . . substitutions in Equations 11, 13, and 17.

15.6.3 Square Brackets

Square brackets (as distinguished from the usual curved parentheses) have a specialized function. They are put around material interpolated into a quotation. They indicate that the bracketed words or symbols are not part of the quoted passage, but are remarks or further explanation added by the quoter or editor.

> The article stated, "When this cycling control [a two-position control for Ward-Leonard dynamometers] is in operation, its resistors replace the usual manually operated field rheostat."

15.7 The Hyphen

15.7.1 The Hyphen in Compound Nouns

A noun consisting of two or more words that name one object is called a compound noun. Some compound nouns are written as separate words; some are hyphenated; and more and more of them are being fused into single words. The only way to tell how any particular compound noun should be written is to look it up in your dictionary or some other reference. Even then, you will find that authorities differ about many words. Here are a few examples of compound nouns.

Separate Words	Hyphenated	Fused
name plate	flare-up	setup (noun)
center punch	light-year	centerboard
center of gravity	lean-to	seaplane
sea otter	double-header	strikebreaker

15.7.2 The Hyphen in Compound Adjectives

An adjective consisting of two or more words that express a unified idea—for instance, *red-nosed*—is called a compound adjective. The words that go to make up a compound adjective may themselves be adjectives, nouns, adverbs, or any other parts of speech.

A compound adjective that comes before the noun it modifies should be hyphenated. Although this rule is commonly relaxed, it should be followed quite rigorously in technical writing. Technical subjects seem to call for a lot of compound adjectives, some of them quite complex; and technical writing must be precise. If you do not hyphenate compound adjectives, your reader will often be momentarily delayed, sometimes actually confused.

Consider this passage:

> ... as given for the adiabatic, no shaft work, constant gravitation potential system.

The reader who is a specialist in thermodynamics quickly spots the compounds. The nonspecialist comes upon these groups of words and discovers at the end of each that it is a compound. This process of comprehension requires unnecessary mental backtracking. The difficulty is aggravated if the compound is separated by the ending of a line. On the other hand, the compounds are immediately evident when they are hyphenated:

> ... as given for the adiabatic, no-shaft-work, constant-gravitation-potential system.

The following examples illustrate some of the temporary misunderstandings that can result from unhyphenated compound adjectives. When you read them, notice that the need for the hyphen can usually be indicated by the reading-aloud test: the words that should be hyphenated are partially fused together as you say them.

Original Example	Comment	Suggested Revision
curved nose cutting tool	For a moment you might read *curved nose-cutting tool.*	curved-nose cutting tool
big city office	A big office in the city, or an office in the big city?	big-city office
carbon containing compounds	Carbon that contains compounds?	carbon-containing compounds
The contractor obtained good results with eight cubic yard scrapers.	Eight scrapers each of 1 cubic yard?	The contractor obtained good results with eight-cubic-yard scrapers.
small time delay transformer	A small transformer that provides time delay?	small-time-delay transformer
prewar quality whiskey	Is this a prewar whiskey of quality? Unfortunately, no.	prewar-quality whiskey

Here is a list of a few representative phrases containing compound adjectives properly hyphenated.

110-volt line	line-of-sight transmission
30-foot depth	short-wave band
160-horsepower engine	high-frequency system
signal-to-noise ratio	long-distance transmission
steady-state operation	information-handling system
single-phase motor	cable-operated brakes
high-fidelity system	spark-plug wrench
frequency-modulation station	clutch-pedal linkage
cathode-ray tube	

Notice that the same words when used as nouns do not require hyphens:

110 volts
30 feet
operation in the steady state
The system has high fidelity.
a cathode ray
The system operates at high frequency.
Power is transmitted over a long distance.
a spark plug
the clutch pedal

The hyphen can be conveniently used as a signal to show that a word will be connected to another word later in the sentence to form a compound adjective.

two-, three-, and four-digit numbers

Exceptions: The hyphen is usually omitted from compound adjectives: (1) When the first word is an adverb ending in -ly, which obviously is going to operate on the word that follows it:

a partly digested fish.

(2) When the compound adjective is a proper noun:

the United States flag.

(3) When the compound adjective is the name of a chemical compound:

a copper sulphate solution.

(4) When the compound adjective is made from a commonly used two-word noun:

an oil filter salesman.

15.7.3 Avoidance of the Hyphen in Compound Adjectives

You will notice that many of the compound adjectives in these examples are made up of *attributive nouns*—that is, nouns used as adjectives. Your writing will be easier to read and clearer if you minimize your use of attributive nouns and the hyphenated compounds that result. You can usually eliminate the need for the hyphen by moving the compound modifier so that it follows its noun instead of preceding it. When the compound comes after its noun, so that it is no longer an adjective, the hyphen is not required either by the rules or by the demands of clarity.

Consider this expression, which actually appeared in a treatise on control systems:

> reference quantity roughness amplitude-dependent quantity roughness amplitude ratio.

After considerable study, you will discover that *ratio* is modified by a long compound adjective composed of all the words that come before it. Although our language makes no provision for hyphens of different lengths and weights, this expression would be clearer if written:

> reference-quantity-roughness-amplitude—dependent-quantity-roughness-amplitude ratio.

But even hyphenated, such a compound is very confusing, because the relationships of the earlier words do not become apparent until you get to the later words. The same idea can be stated quite clearly if the modifier follows the noun:

> ratio of reference-quantity roughness amplitude to dependent-quantity roughness amplitude.

Consider another example:

> It is necessary to eliminate part of the triple superphosphate plant waste disposal cost.

The function of the phrase *triple superphosphate plant waste disposal* is not evident until we reach the word it modifies, *cost*. The relationship is quite vague. Much clearer is:

> It is necessary to eliminate part of the cost of waste disposal at the triple superphosphate plant.

And this phrase:

> magnetic tape mode and channel selecting electronic switch circuits.

benefits by a change:

> circuits for electronic switches to select mode of operation and channel.

The compound adjective does not have to be as long as these to be improved by a shift to the rear.

Original Example	Suggested Revision
output voltage-plate current curve	curve of output voltage vs. plate current
high-velocity-gun-neck angle	neck angle of the high-velocity gun
1½-inch-wide lining	lining 1½ inches wide
air-carbon dioxide mixture	mixture of air and carbon dioxide
air-fuel gas mixture	mixture of air and fuel gas
tire-failure prediction	prediction of tire failure
simplified tube construction (ambiguous)	construction of simplified tubes

15.8 The Apostrophe

If we are to judge by much of the writing coming from both professional men and students, the apostrophe is rapidly going into the discard. This discussion, then, is included only as a word of caution. There are still places where the apostrophe should be used—for example, when one speaks of *my brother's son* or *the company's proposals*.

Of course, the use of the apostrophe can become awkward, and possession can be shown by an indirect expression such as: *the design of the machine tools* instead of *the machine tools' design*.

A point of confusion occurs when the apostrophe is dropped and the possessive is used as an adjective, as when *the company's proposals* is changed to *the company proposals*.

In short, we say that if you do not use an apostrophe to show possession, be prepared to defend your choice.

RECOMMENDED READING

Now that you have studied the principles of technical writing in Chapters 13, 14, and 15, you will be able to appreciate an amusing and instructive little book called *Federal Prose*, by James R. Masterson and Wendell Brooks Phillips, published in 1948 by The University of North Carolina Press.

16. MECHANICS

Every student dreams about the day when he will have a secretary who will attend to all the tiresome mechanical details that come up whenever he has to write a report or paper. This chapter contains advice about a lot of matters that you might think are her business, not yours. But the chances are that when you finally acquire the services of a secretary, she will have been trained at a school that has never heard of technical reporting. She will probably be more interested in various niceties of layout than she will in extreme clarity.

We intend no slight to secretarial schools or their products. But you will find that most secretaries require close supervision and detailed instructions on the subjects treated in this chapter.

16.1 Abbreviations

16.1.1 Use of Abbreviations

An abbreviation will not communicate information to your readers unless it is familiar to them. Thus you should fit your use of abbreviations to the understanding of your intended readers. If in doubt, don't abbreviate. If you have occasion to use an abbreviation repeatedly and you question whether your readers are familiar with it, you can explain it parenthetically the first time it appears.

The propulsion units in ships of this class seldom produce more than 10,000 shp (shaft horsepower).

Abbreviations should be used sparingly in text matter. There are two exceptions to this generally observed rule, and it would be pedantic to insist that terms in either of these groups be spelled out for a technical audience:

(1) Names of units *preceded by numerals;* for instance:

an attenuation of 10 db
a 120-hp engine
The motor was running at 3600 rpm.

But

The decibel is a logarithmic unit.
a fractional-horsepower motor
Motor speed is measured in revolutions per minute.

(2) Terms whose abbreviations have become so well known that they are commonly accepted as part of our everyday vocabulary; for instance:

a-c, d-c, emf, rms, Fig., bmep

On graphs, diagrams, or tables where space is at a premium, abbreviations may be used freely provided their meaning is clear.

16.1.2 Form of Abbreviations

When it comes to the form that abbreviations shall take, chaos reigns. You will often find the same term abbreviated in several different ways in various well-edited publications. But scientists and engineers are more and more falling in line with the American Standards Association's *Abbreviations for Scientific and Engineering Terms* (Z10.1–1941). This pamphlet advocates the following general rules for scientific and technical abbreviations:

(1) Omit periods unless the abbreviation happens to spell a word or would otherwise be confusing without the period.

(2) Do not use capitals unless the word abbreviated is a proper noun.

(3) Use the same abbreviation for singular and plural.

Thus:

cm = centimeter or centimeters
in. = inch or inches
Btu = British thermal unit

The American Standards Association's list of abbreviations is reproduced in the Appendix, Sec. 20.1.

Symbols such as # for *pound* or *number,* ' for *foot,* " for *inch,* / for *per* should not be used in text; they may be used in graphs or tables if there is not room for the corresponding abbreviations.

Exceptions: Two symbols that are commonly considered permissible in text are $ for *dollar* and % for *percent.*

Numerical expressions of temperature usually include a letter to designate the scale, but the degree symbol and the period are preferably omitted.

Water boils at 212 F (100 C).

16.2 Numerals

16.2.1 Use of Numerals

In high school you may have been taught that numbers below 10 should be spelled out, numbers of 10 or higher expressed in Arabic numerals (hereafter called simply *numerals*). But, depending on where you went to school, the dividing line may not have been 10: it may have been 13, or 11, or 3; or perhaps you were told to spell out numbers that can be expressed in one word, or in two words, or in three words. Blind adherence to one of these arbitrary rules might produce:

Radio receiving sets commonly contain anywhere from four to 24 tubes.

The inconsistent expression of these numbers actually obscures the comparison between 4 tubes and 24 tubes. Even the purists will usually say that where numbers below the dividing line (whatever arbitrary line happens to be chosen) are mixed with numbers above it, you may use numerals for all of them.

Now, what is the size of the unit in which a mixture of numbers permits us to use numerals for all of them? A sentence? A paragraph? A page? The authorities do not say.

But we can draw an inference from this widely accepted rule: *In technical and business writing, where there are frequent expressions of*

*quantity, numerals are generally more acceptable than they are in social
or literary writing. Numerals may be used freely to express numbers of
any size unless they would cause confusion or unless a written-out number seems more appropriate* (see Sec. 16.2.3).

16.2.2 Numerals Specifically Acceptable

Numerals are accepted everywhere (except in wedding invitations)
for the following kinds of expressions:

(1) Exact quantities when the number goes with units of measurement.

> a 6-volt storage battery
> The standard size is 8½ by 11 inches.
> a 3-lb hammer
> The temperature fell to 5 F.
> the 60-cycle 110-volt line
> The bond yields 6 percent.
> The fine was $5.

(2) Decimals, fractions, mixed numbers.

> The specific heat of water is 1.0.
> Water is about 1⅓ times as heavy as gasoline.

(3) Numbered objects in a list.

> Fig. 2
> column 3
> page 26
> Chapter 6
> Equation 4
> No. 7

(4) Dates, addresses, and time of day.

> The elevator in the building at 26 Prince St. fell at 2:35 P.M., July 6, 1958.

16.2.3 Numerals Not Acceptable

Numerals are not used:

(1) At the beginning of a sentence. If the number is not too long
or too complicated, it can be spelled out; if this is not feasible, the sentence should be rewritten so that the number is not at the beginning.

(2) Adjacent to other numerals. When two numbers are adjacent
and not separated by punctuation, there is danger of misreading (or mis-
printing) unless one of them is written out.

Original Example	Suggested Revision
24 5-inch straps	twenty-four 5-inch straps *or:* 24 five-inch straps

(3) In round-number approximations. Numerals produce an air of precision that is not suitable for approximate quantities.

> I expect to be in your territory for a week or two.

> The deficit this year will be about $15 billion.

Numbers rounded off to even millions or billions are often easier to comprehend when they are written out as in the second example above. This device should not be used for numbers smaller than a million.

It often seems appropriate to express very small numbers—particularly when they refer to objects or people rather than units—in words rather than numerals.

> This paper synthesizes the findings of three independent investigators.

16.2.4 Numerals: Miscellaneous

(1) Decimal numbers of less than unity should be written with a zero preceding the decimal point. This practice helps to prevent typists from omitting the decimal point, as well as reducing the likelihood of misreading.

(2) Numbers should *not* be expressed in both words and numerals, except perhaps in legal documents. Let us leave these to the lawyers. Do *not* write:

> The trusses will be ready in sixty (60) days.

(3) When you wish to express a range of numbers, use a complete idiom.

Incomplete or Mixed Idiom	Complete Idiom
Delivery is promised in from 30–60 days.	Delivery is promised in from 30 *to* 60 days. *or:* Delivery is promised in 30–60 days.
The work will require between 30–60 days.	The work will require between 30 *and* 60 days. *or:* The work will require 30–60 days.

(4) References to numbered items do not need the word *Number*. Its omission is particularly helpful in the plural form.

Original Example	Suggested Revision
See Drawing No. A-30340.	See Drawing A-30340.
. . . as described in Report No. GP-127.	. . . as described in Report GP-127.
Reports No. 5 and 6 ⎱ Reports Nos. 5 and 6 ⎰	Reports 5 and 6

16.3 Capitals

Initial capital letters used according to conventions with which you are entirely familiar convey certain information. In addition, they give emphasis to the words they begin.

Some technical writers tend to use initial capitals too freely, especially for the names of devices and components. This practice is likely to give undue emphasis to some words. At the same time, if capitals are overused they lose their force and their significance: their ability to emphasize is weakened, and their conventional meanings are beclouded. In general, capitalization should be kept to a minimum.

Original Example	Suggested Revision
The major components of the High Speed Computer are the Arithmetic Element, the Control, the Storage Element, and the Input Output System.	The major components of the high-speed computer are the arithmetic element, the control, the storage element, and the input-output system.

Notice that proper hyphenation of the compound adjectives (see Sec. 15.7.2) performs one of the functions that the original capitalization was probably intended for: to make it clear that certain long names are actually integrated units.

Most, but not all, publications capitalize specific numbered items such as Figure 2 (or Fig. 2) and Table VI. When they occur in text, these expressions are usually repetitions of titles that have appeared capitalized in their original captions. Thus it seems consistent to capitalize them in the text, simply repeating the titles literally. (The same criterion can regulate the choice between *Fig.* and *Figure* in text: simply reproduce the title that appears under the figure, whether it is Fig. 2—which is entirely permissible—or Figure 2.)

16.4 Quotation Marks; Underlining (Italics)

16.4.1 Mechanics

When a single quotation runs more than one paragraph, quotation marks (often called *quotes*) are put at the beginning of each paragraph, but at the end of only the last one.

For some of the functions of quotation marks, underlining (italics in printed matter) is often used instead; see Secs. 16.4.3 and 16.4.5.

16.4.2 Direct Quotations

Whenever you quote somebody else's words, you of course owe it to him to put quotation marks around them and to give him credit for them, no matter how short the passage.

An equally acceptable device is to indent the quoted material inside the margins of the main text and omit the quotation marks. In double-spaced typewritten manuscript, indented quotations are usually single-spaced. In printed material, they are usually set in type smaller than that used for the main text.

16.4.3 Quotation Marks to Distinguish

Quotation marks are often used—and overused—to set aside or distinguish words or phrases. This usage seems to fall into three main categories:

(1) To indicate that a word or phrase is being employed in a new or special or unusual sense, or to introduce a new or strange term. Underlining is sometimes used for the same purpose. The new or strange word should be in quotes (or underlined or italicized) only at its first appearance. From then on, unless confusion would result, it should be considered well enough established to stand on its own feet without special indication.

> Any violation of these arbitrary rules marked a member of the cult as "improper." John had long been considered improper.

(2) Around slangy or slightly disreputable expressions. Quotation marks around slightly off-color expressions serve as an apology. They say, for the writer, "I know better than this, but if you will allow me. . . ." You should probably never use quotation marks this way. Decide beforehand whether the expression is suitable for your intended

audience. If it is, use it without apology and without quotation marks. If it is not, use a different expression.

(3) To emphasize a word or phrase, or to set it apart. Technical writers sometimes put quotation marks around such terms as the names of parts of a system, or the words from a name plate or panel. This indiscriminate use of quotation marks serves to rob them of meaning and to reduce their effectiveness when they are used properly. Often the quotation marks can simply be omitted from such constructions. If some sort of emphasis or separation is required, underlining (italics) is likely to be more suitable than quotes.

Original Example	Suggested Revision
The "accumulator" is connected to the supply.	The accumulator is connected to the supply.
Turn the switch to the "on" position.	Turn the switch to the *on* position.
The first digit column contains a "one."	The first digit column contains a 1.

16.4.4 Quotation Marks in Bibliographical Entries

In formal bibliographical entries, titles of books and periodicals are customarily underlined (italicized), while titles of chapters and articles are enclosed in quotation marks (see Sec. 16.5). Some people use quotation marks instead of underlining for the titles of books and periodicals.

16.4.5 Words Referred to as Words

When you wish to mention a word as a word—as a vocabulary term— rather than to refer to its meaning, you can either underline (italicize) the word or enclose it in quotes.

My wife thinks *stink* is an ugly word.
  (or . . . "stink" . . .)

16.5 Bibliographies

16.5.1 Form of Bibliographical Entries

Technical reports and papers frequently carry bibliographies. If you have looked critically at the bibliographies in various publications, you have discovered that there is little uniformity from one publication to another. If you are writing for any particular publication, you will do well to follow its style.

But in general a bibliographical entry is successful if it enables the reader to find the cited material with a minimum of trouble; the order of the parts and the punctuation used to separate them is relatively unimportant. The required information—conventionally given in this order—usually is:

Books	Magazine or Journal Articles
Author	Author
Title	Title of article
(Place of publication)	Name of magazine or journal
Publisher	Volume number, date of issue, or both
Date	Pages

Encyclopedia Articles	Reports
Title of article	Author
Name of encyclopedia	Title
Edition number	Name of issuing organization
Date	Report number
Volume number	Date
Pages	

Here are examples of acceptable bibliographical entries:

(1) Book

Kunin, R., and Myers, R. J. *Ion Exchange Resins.* New York: John Wiley and Sons, Inc., 1950.

(2) Magazine and journal articles

Farmer, L. "The Old People." *Harper's Magazine* (Dec. 1951), 79–82.

Dillinger, P. B. "The Propagation of Radio Waves," *Transactions of the AIEE,* LVIII (1939), 79–99.

(3) Encyclopedia article

"Radium." *Encyclopaedia Britannica,* 14 ed. (1929), XVIII, 906–908.

(4) Report

Carmichael, T. J. *Elastic Creep of Automobile Tires.* General Motors Proving Ground Report 22.1357 (1945).

Anonymous articles from magazines or other publications are treated in the same way as the encyclopedia example above, with the title first.

Some publications list joint authors this way:

Jones, P. D., H. R. Smith, and R. D. Leffingwell.

The different order for surnames and initials seems to be a needless inconsistency; we recommend instead:

Jones, P. D., Smith, H. R., and Leffingwell, R. D.

Titles of books, magazines, and articles are customarily underlined or put in quotation marks to distinguish them from surrounding text (see Sec. 16.4). In a formal bibliography, one expects to see titles, and they hardly need to be distinguished by special typography. Some publications, particularly typewritten reports, simply ignore the underlining convention in their bibliographies.

Whatever bibliographical form you choose, use it consistently for any one document. For sample bibliographies see pages 96 and 371.

16.5.2 Arrangement of Bibliographies

The entries in a bibliography may be arranged in various ways. The simplest and most usual is a single list, with authors' surnames and titles of anonymous articles intermixed in alphabetical sequence.

Longer bibliographies are sometimes broken up into separate lists of books, articles, pamphlets, or other forms of publication. Then again, it may be helpful to your readers to break your bibliography into separate lists by topics in a long report or paper.

Another acceptable sequence for bibliographical entries is the order in which you refer to them. This order is appropriate particularly if you use the bibliography instead of individual footnotes or citations (see Sec. 16.6.2).

16.6 Footnotes (Citation)

16.6.1 What to Credit

Remember that you are obligated to give credit not only for sequences of *words* that you have borrowed, but also for sequences, or essential arrangements, of *ideas*. If you particularly want your readers to know who the original author was, or if his name will lend weight and authority to your statement, you can make your citation right in the text.

Usually, though, the citation is a routine matter, and a footnote is a convenient way to take care of it.

Authors of papers based largely on library research often wonder how frequent their footnotes must be. Must every sentence have a footnote giving the source of its information? Or is one general statement of indebtedness sufficient? The answer will usually be a compromise between these two extremes. If you follow the rule below, you will probably fulfill your obligations without cluttering your manuscript with needless footnotes.

To give credit for an arrangement of ideas—that is, for a considerable mass of information—use one general, over-all citation. To give credit for a specific arrangement of words or lines—that is, for a verbatim quotation or for the reproduction of a drawing—provide a citation for each item.

Information that is common knowledge—that you might find in any of several sources—does not need to be credited unless you present it in a verbatim quotation.

16.6.2 Systems for Citation

Two systems for citing references are in common use. A third, which is a sort of compromise between the first two, has advantages that are making it increasingly popular.

(1) *Full bibliographical notes.* Each superscript in the text refers to a note, which may be at the foot of the page or in a group at the end of the chapter or the end of the paper (but separate from the bibliography). The note for the first reference to each source is a full bibliographical entry, with the addition of specific page numbers. (The order of the items in notes often differs from the conventional order in bibliographies: the title may precede the author's name, and the author's given name or initials may precede his surname.) Succeeding notes referring to the same source may be abbreviated in any of the several ways described in most handbooks. The terms *ibid.* (in the same place) and *loc. cit.* (in the place already mentioned) may be used if there is no doubt about what they refer to. Perhaps better, the bibliographical entry may be shortened down to the point where it carries just enough information to identify its reference: if only one work of an author is

referred to, his surname alone may be sufficient; or maybe a shortened form of the title, containing only key words, must be added.

This system is the conventional one in most of the learned journals. It is complete, explicit, and clear. But it is cumbersome and it involves a lot of duplication; and if the notes are put at the foot of each page, they produce a cluttered appearance.

(2) *Bibliography instead of notes.* Each superscript in the text refers to the similarly numbered entry in the bibliography. This system, which is used by a number of the technical journals, is neat and convenient, but it does not provide for the listing of specific page numbers for each reference.

(3) *Footnotes referring to bibliography.* Each superscript refers to a note (at the foot of the page or grouped) that cites a bibliography entry *by number* and gives a specific page number. For example:

. . . . . . [1] . . . . .
. . . .
. . . . [2]
. . . .

_____

[1] Reference 6, p. 29.
[2] Reference 14, pp. 142–150.

This system is the same as No. 1 except that bibliography numbers are used instead of titles. It is less cumbersome than No. 1; yet it permits references to specific page numbers.

If you choose a system that does not use actual footnotes, place one footnote at the bottom of the page carrying the first superscript, and in this footnote explain the system you are using and tell your readers where to look for the references. For instance, you might say

[1] Superscripts refer to similarly numbered entries in the Bibliography.

or

[1] Superscripts refer to notes at the end of each chapter.

This explanation will prevent your readers from referring to the bibliography when they should be referring to notes, or from looking for notes that are not there.

Superscript numerals are generally preferable to asterisks, daggers, or other symbols for referring to notes, particularly when there are several references on one page. A new series starting with 1 may be used for each page or each chapter, or a single series may be used for the entire paper or report.

16.7 Heading Systems

Section 2.8 stressed the idea that headings and subheadings should be used freely, and that they should make evident the structure of the paper or report. Therefore it is very important to employ a system of headings in which the relative weights of the various headings, and their relationships to each other, are abundantly clear. Three effective systems are described in Secs. 16.7.1–16.7.3, below.

Of these schemes, the first two are customarily used for outlines as well as text. The third—a less formal one—is suitable for text but not for outlines.

The examples that follow are set up with acceptable arrangements of typography and indentation. But of course many other arrangements are entirely suitable for the same basic schemes. Just be sure that the typography and indentation you choose contribute to the clarity and information-content of your heading system.

16.7.1 The Decimal System

The system of headings used in this book is commonly called the *decimal system,* although the periods are really simply separators, not decimal points. The numbers and headings are arranged this way:

1. FIRST-DEGREE HEADING
   1.1 Second-degree Heading
   1.2 Second-degree Heading
     1.2.1 Third-degree Heading
     1.2.2 Third-degree Heading
   1.3 Second-degree Heading

2. FIRST-DEGREE HEADING
   Etc.

The number of degrees may be extended at will, of course, by the addition of more digits and more points. If you use this system for an outline, you may want six or more degrees, but for headings in a report or paper, three or four are usually enough.

The decimal system is becoming increasingly popular. It is a rigorous system that never leaves any doubt about the relative weight of any heading. Furthermore, when you come upon an isolated decimal-system subheading—no matter of what degree—you know at once how it fits into the main scheme.

Some users of the decimal system put a point only after the first-degree digit, running all lighter-weight digits together, this way:

1.
  1.1
  1.2
    1.21
    1.22
      1.221
      1.222
    1.23
  1.3
2.

This scheme is all right so long as there are not more than nine headings of the same degree in one group. But if there should be more than nine, ambiguity occurs: the heading 1.12, for instance, might then belong in either of two series:

```
1.                          1.
   1.1                         1.1
   1.2                            1.11
     .                            1.12
     .           or
     .
   1.9
   1.10
   1.11
   1.12
```

Thus it is generally safer to add a point for each additional degree after the second; and it is essential whenever there are more than nine headings of the same degree in any one group.

16.7.2 The Numeral-Letter System

Probably the commonest system of designations for outline headings uses a sequence of Roman numerals, capital letters, Arabic numerals, and lower-case letters.

I. FIRST-DEGREE HEADING
  A. Second-degree Heading
  B. Second-degree Heading
    1. Third-degree Heading
    2. Third-degree Heading
      a. Fourth-degree Heading
      b. Fourth-degree Heading
    3. Third-degree Heading
  C. Second-degree Heading
II. FIRST-DEGREE HEADING
  Etc.

The number of degrees may be extended by the addition of further Arabic numerals and lower-case letters in parentheses.

This system suffers the disadvantage that isolated subheadings are not oriented in the main scheme. When you come upon a heading numbered 3, for instance, you do not know whether 3 belongs under A, B, or C, etc.; and you do not know what Roman numeral the capital letter falls under. To find out, you must go backward until you come to a first-degree heading.

16.7.3 Typography-Indentation Systems

The relative weights of various headings may be indicated by a consistent arrangement of typography and indentation. Such systems are not as rigorous as the ones described in the two preceding sections, and they are hardly suitable for outlines. But they are quite effective for text headings, particularly for relatively short and informal reports or papers.

One possible arrangement is shown at the top of the next page. Systems similar to this one are used in the Preface of this book and in some of the specimen reports in the Appendix. Of course many other variations are acceptable.

FIRST-DEGREE HEADING
(Centered; all capitals; underlined.)

SECOND-DEGREE HEADING
(At left margin; all capitals; underlined.)

Third-degree Heading
(Indented; initial capitals; not underlined.)

16.7.4 Physical Arrangement of Headings

No matter what system of headings you use, you can improve its effectiveness by careful attention to physical arrangement.

(1) Headings of all degrees serve as signposts. They are effective only if they stand out from the surrounding text. To make them conspicuous:

(a) Put every heading, no matter of what degree, on a line by itself. Do not start a sentence on the line occupied by a heading.

(b) *Separate every heading or subheading from following text by two typewriter spaces (lines); separate every heading or subheading from preceding text by at least three typewriter spaces.* This spacing not only makes the heading stand out; it also ties the heading to the material with which it is logically connected and separates it from the preceding material.

(2) In reports or documents of any length, main (first-degree) headings usually go at the top of a new page.

(3) In outlines, the "text" (explanatory material) is usually indented as far as the heading under which it falls. Although the headings you use in a report or paper may be indented just as if they were in an outline, the text that comes under them should usually be carried to the left-hand margin (except, of course, for the first lines of paragraphs) no matter how far the heading is indented. Indentation of text under headings wastes paper and tends to spread things out unduly.

16.8 Typing

16.8.1 Line Spacing

Manuscripts for publication are always typed double-spaced. Business letters are customarily single-spaced. Reports may be either double-spaced or single-spaced, depending on the copy. Any material that contains equations, superscripts, or subscripts is easier to read if it is double-spaced. Reports or papers submitted to your instructors should be double-spaced to facilitate marking and correction.

16.8.2 Paragraph Indentation

In double-spaced copy the first line of each paragraph is customarily indented, say five letter spaces.

In single-spaced copy a double space is left between paragraphs. In block-style single-spaced typing—popular for business letters—the paragraph is not indented, the double space serving as the only indication of a new paragraph. If one sentence ends at the bottom of a page and another one begins at the top of the next, there is no way for the reader to tell whether this second sentence begins a new paragraph or is part of the old one. Therefore in technical writing, where precision is more important than style, the first line of every paragraph should be indented whether the copy is double-spaced or single-spaced.

16.9 Binding Margin

Most organizations bind their reports—at least the longer, more formal ones—in fairly well standardized cardboard covers. These covers have two folds about an inch wide between which the pages are fastened. The top fold conceals at least ⅞ inch of the left-hand edge of the page. This concealed edge is considerably wider in the interior of thick reports, because their pages cannot be turned back sharply.

Therefore when you are preparing sheets of any kind—text, graphs, or drawings—that are to be bound into ordinary report covers, leave a binding margin of at least 1¼ inches, and preferably 1½ inches, at the left edge. Be particularly careful about graphs drawn on commercial graph paper, which often has a left-hand border of less than ¾ inch. We have seen curves plotted across the whole grid, right out to the border, with the scale in the border. When a curve-sheet like this is bound into a report, the vertical scale is completely hidden from view. To avoid this serious fault, you can either trace the graph on plain paper with a suitable margin, or you can get commercial graph paper with extra-wide borders (see Sec. 18.5).

16.10 Page Numbering

Two systems are in use for the numbering of pages in books and reports. In the more common of these, the preliminary pages (title page, preface, table of contents, and so forth) are numbered in one series of small Roman numerals; the main body is numbered in a separate series of Arabic numerals. In the other system, which is used occasionally for books, oftener for reports, all the pages are numbered consecutively in one series of Arabic numerals. The single series is in some ways more convenient for the reader.

Whichever system you use, the title page is counted as the first page (i or 1), although no number is placed on it.

On all ordinary pages the number usually goes at the *top outer corner*. The number is often omitted from pages that start with a centered main heading, but it is preferable, for the convenience of the reader, to put numbers at the *bottom center* of these pages.

16.11 Methods of Reproduction

This is not the place for an extended treatise on printing processes, but you will probably be interested in some general information about the various ways in which reports can be reproduced.

16.11.1 Printing Processes

(1) *Carbon Copies.*

When only a few copies—say half a dozen—of a report are to be made for internal distribution, ordinary carbon-paper copies of the text may be adequate. Carbon copies are by no means elegant; they tend to smudge; and the later ones are blurry. But they are cheap and convenient when you do not have to make an impression.

(2) *Hectograph.*

In the hectograph (or Ditto) process, the copy is typed or drawn on a master—a sheet of paper that receives and holds all the pigment that is later transferred to the copies. In the *gelatin* method, a special ribbon is used in the typewriter. After the master has been typed, it is laid face down on a gelatin slab, its positive image being transferred to the slab in negative. Sheets of paper pressed to the slab then pick up a positive print.

Except for very small installations, the gelatin method has been largely superseded by the *liquid* or *spirit* method. In this process a piece of special carbon paper that contains the pigment is put face up behind the master while the copy is typed or drawn on it. Pressure on the face of the master picks up a mirror image on the back. In the printing press this negative image is partially dissolved by a solution of alcohol and water and transferred directly as a positive image to the copies.

The hectograph process is convenient, because text and rough sketches can readily be put on the same page. The usual color is purple, but several other colors are available, and they can be mixed on the same page. The equipment is comparatively inexpensive and does not require highly trained operators.

On the other hand, the masters are very messy to work with, and the printed image is weak and fuzzy. Because no pigment is available besides what is originally on the master, not more than a couple of hundred copies can be made from each master.

(3) *Mimeograph.*

In the Mimeograph process the copy is put onto a stencil that consists of a thin, porous sheet covered with a special wax that is impervious to ink. Typing on the stencil (with the typewriter ribbon inoperative) or scratching on it with a special stylus removes the wax from the areas where the image is to appear. The stencil is then mounted on a drum that has an inked surface and rolled across the paper. Wherever the wax has been removed from the stencil, ink seeps through and prints on the paper.

Mimeograph presses are relatively inexpensive and easy to use. The printed image is black but somewhat fuzzy. Several thousand copies can be made from one stencil.

It is very difficult to produce successful sketches on Mimeograph, and the paper that must be used is rather porous and weak.

(4) *Direct Offset (Multilith).*

The highest-quality office duplicating process is a form of offset lithography; the best known direct-offset equipment is trade-named Multilith. In this process the image (positive) is typed with a special ribbon or drawn onto an ink-repellent paper or plastic "plate." When an inked roller in the press goes over this plate, ink is deposited on the image, repelled by the rest of the plate. The positive ink image is then picked up by another roller, on whose surface it presents a negative image. This roller is rolled over the paper, laying down a positive image. (The term *offset* refers to the intermediate process of picking up the image on a roller before it is impressed on the paper. If this step were omitted, and the original positive ink image were transmitted directly to the paper, it would appear as a negative.)

Direct-offset printing is black and clear-cut; it is virtually as good as the copy from which it is made. Detailed drawings can be put right in with the text, and, with the adjunct of photographically produced (photo-offset) plates, even halftone illustrations can be included. There is no reasonable limit to the number of copies that can be made from one master. Any kind of paper and ink of any color may be used.

Direct offset has only two disadvantages: (a) The smallest press available is still quite expensive, so that its purchase is not economical unless there is enough work to keep it reasonably busy. (b) An unskilled operator cannot produce the best-quality results.

(5) *Photo-offset.*

Photo-offset printing (also known as planographing or photolithography) is a full-fledged printing-plant process. The printing operation itself is essentially the same as in direct offset, except that the presses are much larger; but the image is put on the plate photographically instead of directly.

Copy that has been prepared by typing, drawing, letter-press printing (see below)—or any other method—is photographed, with any desired amount of reduction or enlargement. The resultant negative is printed onto a zinc, aluminum, plastic, or paper plate covered with a photosensitive emulsion. The surface of the plate is ink-repellent except for the area of the positive image. Copies are printed from this plate in an offset press just as in the direct-offset process described above.

Photo-offset can produce very high-grade results; in fact it is used for printing many fine books and magazines. It is particularly flexible and convenient for combinations of text and line drawings, and it reproduces halftones quite well. Because of the initial cost of preparing the negative and the plate, photo-offset is not economical unless perhaps a hundred or more copies are required.

(6) *Letterpress.*

In letterpress printing (also a printing-plant process), the ink is transferred to the paper from metal slugs or plates that have a negative image of the copy raised above the surrounding level. Text is set in movable type, usually by machine; special effects and rules are set by hand; and drawings or halftones are printed from acid-etched metal plates.

Letterpress printing can produce very high-grade results. It is not as convenient as photo-offset for mixtures of text and line drawings, and its plates usually cost considerably more than photo-offset plates. It is not economical unless at least several hundred copies are being run.

16.11.2 Photographic Processes

Drawings and illustrations, and in fact text, can be reproduced in small quantities by several photographic processes.

(1) *Blueprinting.*

In blueprinting, a direct contact print is made from the original copy (which must be on translucent paper) onto the photosensitive blueprint paper, which is then developed in an aqueous solution. The resulting copies are negative, white lines on a blue background, unless an intermediate negative is made. The copies are permanent. For most purposes blueprinting has been largely superseded by the more convenient ammonia-vapor or Ozalid process.

(2) *Ozalid.*

The Ozalid process (also known as black-and-white, blue-line, black-line, white-print, and ammonia-vapor process) is the same as blueprinting except that: (a) the prints are positive; and (b) they are developed dry, in ammonia vapor, so that they are available immediately after printing. Intermediate sepia (translucent) copies permit a series of prints with any desired variations, and fairly good halftones can be made on special paper from film positives.

This process is highly flexible and very convenient. It is used primarily for the duplication of drawings and graphs, but it can be used for text. *Typewritten copy that is to be reproduced by Ozalid should be carbon backed (typed with a sheet of carbon paper facing the back of the page) on translucent paper without a watermark.*

Ozalid prints fade slowly over a period of years.

When more than fifty or a hundred copies of a line drawing are required, photo-offset printing costs no more and is of better quality than Ozalid. For text pages, hectograph, Mimeograph, or direct offset is cheaper when more than about half a dozen copies are required.

(3) *Photostat.*

The photostat process is essentially the same as ordinary photography except that the negative is made of paper. Reproductions are permanent, of better quality than Ozalid, and also more expensive. The process is appropriate only for quantities of a few dozen or less.

(4) *Photography.*

You are familiar with conventional photography. It is the highest-quality and most expensive method of this group. It is appropriate only for quantities of a few dozen or less.

17. TABLES

17.1 The Use of Tables

Numerical data presented in exposition form are very difficult to assimilate and interpret. For example, how much does this passage (adapted from an actual report) convey to you on first reading?

> Out of ninety tubes tested, sixty A7A's had interfaces, ten E7A's had interfaces, and ten each A7A and E7A had no interface.

Now take a look, even a quick one, at the same information tabulated:

Table 1 : Formation of Cathode Interface

Tube Type	Interface	
	Number With	Number Without
A7A	60	10
E7A	10	10

At a glance, you take in all the numerical information and get a good idea of its significance. And much as this very small and simple set of data is clarified by tabulation, larger sets benefit even more.

When the really interested reader comes upon a prose presentation of data that he cannot readily understand, what does he do? He stops and tabulates the figures, either mentally or actually on paper, for himself; or perhaps he even plots them (see Chapter 18). It is more considerate and more efficient and more accurate for the author to supply the tabulation (or the plot) once and for all, for all of his readers. We urge you to use tables freely as a means of communicating information efficiently.

17.2 The Place of Tables

For the purposes of this book, we can divide tables into two main categories: those that form an integral part of the presentation of ideas, and those that are included simply for record purposes. The chief differences in the treatment of these two classes are that (1) the "record" table should usually be tucked out of the way in an appendix, while the "integral" table is most useful and most convenient if it appears at the appropriate place in the text; and (2) the record table may contain more figures than the integral table. We are most interested in the integral tables, but the principles discussed in this chapter apply to both kinds.

Tables are serially numbered, often in Roman numerals, and usually in a series separate from the series of Arabic numerals used for all the illustrative material, or *figures*. Sometimes, however, the tables are numbered in the main series of figures, and are labeled "Figure 10" rather than "Table X."

17.3 General Principles

17.3.1 Conciseness

Tables, like other forms of communication, are clearer and easier to understand if they are short. If a table you are constructing seems forbiddingly long, try breaking it up into two or more shorter ones. Or, if you must include a long table for record purposes, put it into an appendix, and quote brief excerpts from it in your text (see Secs. 7.2 and 7.4).

By all means, include no column of information in a table unless it has a direct bearing on your subject. It is almost safe to say, include no column of information unless it is specifically referred to in the text.

17.3.2 Titles and Headings

Every table should have a title. Like all other titles, it should be clear and as brief as it can be yet still descriptive of the contents of the table (see Sec. 2.14). Although the reader may not get a *complete* understanding of the nature of the table without reading the accompanying text, he should get a general or basic idea of it from the title alone.

The conventional position for the title is above the table, with the table number immediately preceding the descriptive title. If the tables are numbered in the main series of figures, however, the title and figure number should go beneath the table, in the conventional position for figure titles.

Similarly, every column and every row in the table should have a clear, concise, descriptive heading. In order to save space, the words in a column heading may often be "stacked up," like those over the first two columns of Table 2.

17.3.3 Units

Never fail to name units of measurement. Usually the column or row heading is the convenient and efficient place to specify units; see Tables 2, 3, 7, and 10. On the other hand, if all the figures in the table are in the same units, the designation may be implicit in the main title. Sometimes you will see the name of the unit following each of the figures, as in Table 4. This position is likely to result in needless repetition, and is generally less workmanlike than the other two. However, in tables of sums of money, the dollar sign may well go right in the columns, preceding the figures in the first and last lines.

17.4 Some Specific Suggestions

17.4.1 Underlining of Column Headings

The most precise way of connecting column headings with the figures to which they apply is by means of vertical ruling, or boxing, as in Tables 4, 5, 6, and 7. But this boxing entails considerable complication and labor, particularly when the table is typewritten. An acceptably precise arrangement of column headings illustrated in Table 2 uses only horizontal ruling that can be easily made on the typewriter.

Table 2.   Gasoline Analyses

Sample No.	Gravity, °API	ASTM Distillation, °F					Octane Number	
		IBP	10%	50%	90%	EP	Motor	Research
1	60.2	98	144	225	319	386	79	87
2	64.9	102	133	206	302	378	85	95
3	68.1	98	126	220	340	378	81	90
4	63.5	99	141	211	289	356	80	83
5	62.0	96	127	195	298	368	80	89

Notice in particular that the length of each of the horizontal rules shows the extent, or the number of columns, to which its heading applies.

A frequent practice is to run the horizontal ruling under headings all the way across the table, like this:

Sample No.	Gravity, °API	ASTM Distillation, °F					Octane Number	
		IBP	10%	50%	90%	EP	Motor	Research
1	60.2	98	144	225	319	386	79	87

Etc.

What each heading covers is now by no means so clear.   The horizontal ruling should be put to some use besides simply separation of the headings from the body of the table.

17.4.2 Columniation

In a column of figures of like units, the decimal points should be lined up in the conventional way.   But in a column of unlike units, particularly when the magnitudes differ greatly, it is wasteful of space and illogical to align the decimal points; the numerals should be centered in the columns, as shown in Table 3.

Table 3.   Analysis of Used Oil

Sulfur, percent	0.22
Iron, percent	0.06
Lead, percent	0.006
Viscosity @ 100 F, Saybolt seconds	642
Viscosity @ 210 F, Saybolt seconds	73
Viscosity Index	104

17.4.3 Duplicate Entries in Adjacent Columns

It is best to avoid duplicate entries in adjacent parallel columns. You will often see tables constructed as in Table 4.

Table 4. Specifications of Rumbler Experimental Car

	Car A	Car B
Wheelbase	85 in.	85 in.
Tread	48 in.	48 in.
Overall length	146 in.	146 in.
Overall width	63 in.	63 in.
Weight	1450 lb	1550 lb
Seat width	46 in.	46 in.
Overall height	54 in.	54 in.
Head room	31 in.	31 in.
Leg room	28 in.	28 in.
Engine hp	18	36
Trans. speeds for'd.	3	4
Top speed	60–65 mph	65–70 mph
Fuel economy	45–50 mpg	35–40 mpg
Tire mileage	50,000 or more	50,000 or more
Approx. price	$1200	$1300

Notice that the differences between Car A and Car B fade into the background of duplicate entries. The distinguishing characteristics are by no means immediately apparent; you have to search them out.

Now look at this table rearranged (Table 5) with duplicate entries centered between the columns to which they apply.

Table 5. Specifications of Rumbler Experimental Car (Revised)

	Car A	Car B
Wheelbase, in.	85	
Tread, in.	48	
Overall length, in.	146	
Overall width, in.	63	
Weight, lb	1450	1550
Seat width, in.	46	
Overall height, in.	54	
Head room, in.	31	
Leg room, in.	28	
Engine hp	18	36
Trans. speeds for'd.	3	4
Top speed, mph	60–65	65–70
Fuel economy, mpg	45–50	35–40
Tire mileage	50,000 or more	
Approx. price	$1200	$1300

A comparison of the two cars is now easy and automatic; it becomes immediately obvious that they are identical except for their engines and transmissions. The increased prominence of the differing entries suggests further revisions whose need was not nearly so apparent in the original table: the *weight* line might well be put beneath the *transmission speed* line, and the *tire mileage* line might be moved to the end of the table.

 Entries duplicated in adjacent columns can mask not only *differences*, but also *similarities*. Consider Table 6:

Table 6.   Rumbler Truck Engines

Truck Model	120	130	140	150	160	170	180
Bore, in.	$3\frac{1}{4}$	$3\frac{1}{4}$	$3\frac{1}{4}$	$3\frac{7}{16}$	$3\frac{7}{16}$	$3\frac{3}{4}$	$3\frac{3}{4}$
Stroke, in.	$4\frac{3}{8}$	$4\frac{5}{8}$	$4\frac{5}{8}$	$4\frac{1}{4}$	$4\frac{1}{2}$	$4\frac{5}{8}$	5
Displacement, cu in.	218	230	230	237	251	306	331
Compression ratio	8.6	8.5	9.2	8.6	8.6	8.5	8.5
Max. gross hp	98	100	105	110	115	125	130
Number main bearings	4	4	4	4	4	7	7

Now look at Table 7, a revised version of Table 6.

Table 7.   Rumbler Truck Engines (Revised)

Truck Model	120	130	140	150	160	170	180
Bore, in.	$3\frac{1}{4}$			$3\frac{7}{16}$		$3\frac{3}{4}$	
Stroke, in.	$4\frac{3}{8}$	$4\frac{5}{8}$		$4\frac{1}{4}$	$4\frac{1}{2}$	$4\frac{5}{8}$	5
Displacement, cu in.	218	230		237	251	306	331
Compression ratio	8.6	8.5	9.2	8.6		8.5	
Max. gross hp	98	100	105	110	115	125	130
Number main bearings	4					7	

A lot of information about these engines that was buried in the original table makes itself almost immediately apparent in this revised version: Three basic cylinder blocks (three bores) are shared by the seven engines.   Each of these blocks is furnished with crankshafts of two different strokes, providing engines of six displacements.   Model 140 is apparently the same as model 130 except that it has a higher compression ratio and consequently greater power output.   The two smaller blocks have 4 main bearings, the large block 7.

Caution: The device of centering entries between columns does not work clearly unless the table is completely boxed.

17.4.4 Duplicate Entries in Successive Lines

You can usually replace columns of ditto marks (or literally repeated entries) by a more informative scheme. Table 8 is adapted from a report on some experimental tank wheels.

Table 8.   Performance of Tank Bogie Wheels

Wheel No.	Position	Type Weld	Miles to Failure
90	1L	Butt	1540
91	2R	"	1734
92	3L	"	1307
93	4R	"	1915
94	5L	"	2060
95	1R	Lap	2758
96	2L	"	2592
97	3R	"	2621
98	4L	"	3414
99	5R	"	2866

This arrangement masks the fact that one of the important purposes of the test was to compare the durability of the two types of welds. One way to clarify this table is to remove the *type-weld* column and substitute horizontal subheads for it, as in Table 9.

Table 9.   Performance of Tank Bogie Wheels (Revised)

Wheel No.	Position	Miles to Failure
Butt-welded Wheels		
90	1L	1540
91	2R	1734
92	3L	1307
93	4R	1915
94	5L	2060
Avg		1711
Lap-welded Wheels		
95	1R	2758
96	2L	2592
97	3R	2621
98	4L	3414
99	5R	2866
Avg		2850

The more obvious separation of the wheels into two groups suggests the worth of the two *average-mileage* entries, which have been added.

Note that the first horizontal subhead goes *below* the column headings.   (For some reason that has no basis in logic, you will sometimes find the first subhead above the column headings.)

Another effective substitute for the column of dittos is illustrated in Table 10.   This scheme requires boxing.

Table 10.   Performance of Tank Bogie Wheels (Revised)

Type Weld	Wheel No.	Position	Miles to Failure
Butt	90	1L	1540
	91	2R	1734
	92	3L	1307
	93	4R	1915
	94	5L	2060
	Avg		1711
Lap	95	1R	2758
	96	2L	2592
	97	3R	2621
	98	4L	3414
	99	5R	2866
	Avg		2850

17.4.5 Adjacent Columns for Numbers to be Compared

In a table containing sets of numbers that are to be compared, you can ease the reader's task, and make the comparison more evident, by arranging them in adjacent columns rather than stringing them out in a single column.   Table 11, from a report on possible schemes for a manufacturing process, obscures comparison.

Table 11.   Cost Per Record

Single-opening Press	
Coating Contracted	
1 shift	$0.0032
2 shifts	0.0030
Coating in Shop	
1 shift	0.0029
2 shifts	0.0027
Double-opening Press	
Coating Contracted	
1 shift	0.0031
2 shifts	0.0029
Coating in Shop	
1 shift	0.0028
2 shifts	0.0026

The same data rearranged in adjacent columns, Table 12, permits an easy comparison of the costs of the various schemes.

Table 12.   Cost Per Record (Revised)

	Coating Contracted		Coating in Shop	
	1 Shift	2 Shifts	1 Shift	2 Shifts
Single-opening press	$0.0032	$0.0030	$0.0029	$0.0027
Double-opening press	0.0031	0.0029	0.0028	0.0026

18. VISUAL PRESENTATION OF INFORMATION

18.1 The Use of Visual Presentation

Very important tools for technical reporting are the visual or graphical aids—pictures, diagrams, and graphs. Often a glance at a schematic diagram will reveal an arrangement, or a glance at a curve will show a relationship, that words alone could never make really clear. You should by all means use the visual aids freely whenever they will help your reader.

The classical view was that graphs and drawings were strictly to *supplement* the verbal presentation of information. But if you can give your reader a grasp of a complicated machine most clearly and most easily by means of a drawing, why burden him with a lengthy word description besides? If a curve that shows the relationship between some data also shows their numerical values with sufficient accuracy, why clutter up your report with a table of those same values? A growing tendency is to let visual presentations *supplant* verbal ones as well as supplement them.

But if your verbal exposition is to be logically complete, it must contain at least the fundamental description, or definition, discussed in Sec. 2.4. For instance, it is insufficient to say simply:

The essential characteristics of the d'Arsonval movement are shown in Fig. x.

A statement that is not very much longer but a great deal more satisfying to the reader might run this way:

> The d'Arsonval movement, as shown in Fig. x, is basically a coil pivoted in a permanent magnetic field. A torque proportional to current flowing in the coil is resisted by springs. A pointer attached to the coil indicates the displacement of the coil and thus the magnitude of the current.

Fig. x, of course, fills in a lot of details not covered in this basic definition.

18.2 The Place of Visual Presentation

In most technical reports and papers the figures are an integral part of the presentation. Therefore the most useful place to put them is right with the text they illustrate. But if they are inconveniently large or bulky, or if one or more of them is referred to several times in different parts of the text, it may be more convenient to group them all together following the text. If you refer to a figure that is neither nearby nor in a group at the end, specify not only the figure number but also the page number. Figures, such as working drawings, that are included only for record purposes can well be put at the end, in an appendix.

All the figures—graphs, drawings, diagrams, photographs, maps— are usually numbered in one series of Arabic numerals. Sometimes in a long work such as a textbook a separate series is used for each chapter, with the chapter number preceding each individual number, thus: 1–1, 1–2, 1–3; 2–1, 2–2, 2–3; etc. Whatever system you use, be sure that you never assign the same number to two different figures in one report or paper.

18.3 Reference to Figures

Remember that every figure must be integrated into the verbal presentation by means of a specific reference in the text. The position of this reference is very important:

(1) *The reference should precede the figure whenever possible.* A drawing or curve that has not been mentioned in the text interrupts the

reader's train of thought; it mystifies and annoys him. He is likely to overlook its significant features. On the other hand, if the figure comes after the reference the reader will obey instructions to refer to it at the appropriate time. He will not be interrupted, and he will know what to look for in the figure.

(2) *The reference should be made as early in the discussion as it appropriately can be.* To learn at the end of a complicated and tedious description that "the details of this construction are clearly shown in the drawing on the next page" is of very little help, because it comes too late. The right time for the reader to look at the drawing is while he is reading the description.

18.4 General Principles

18.4.1 Simplicity

Although their purpose is usually to clarify and facilitate the communication of information, the visual aids can suffer from the same fault that characterizes so many technical reports: the burial of the main, basic idea under a lot of details. When you construct a graph or a drawing, do not obscure the main idea by surrounding it with unnecessary details. *Make your graphical presentations as simple and as open and as bold as you can.*

Sometimes the figures that you prepare (or obtain) will be reduced in the published version of your paper or report. There is always the danger that lettering or other details will not be legible after the reduction. Therefore, when you are preparing figures for publication, try to plan them specifically for reduction to the final size. Be sure that the lettering is large enough to be easily legible after reduction. To make all the drawings in a paper or report look uniform, it is a good idea to standardize on one reduction factor and one series of letter sizes for all the drawings.

18.4.2 Titles; Independence

Every figure should have a descriptive title in addition to the figure number. Number and title are usually placed beneath the figure. How much information should the title supply? Certainly it should describe the basic nature of the figure, if for no other reason than for the benefit of those "readers" who look only at the pictures. But how much more information should it carry?

Some organizations insist that every drawing and every graph or curve sheet be able to "stand alone"; that is, be *entirely comprehensible* to someone who has only that sheet, and no accompanying text or explanation. If this criterion is to be met, each sheet must supply a lot of background, or orientation, information in addition to its specific title. For instance, if it were being sent out by itself, the curve sheet of Fig. 6 on page 230 would carry some or all of the following information in addition to what it has: car numbers; weight and axle ratios of cars; odometer readings; dates of tests; temperature, wind direction and velocity, and weather conditions during tests; grade of oil in engines; and fuel used. If the sheet is going to be distributed separately—by itself— then it needs this sort of information in order to be meaningful. On the other hand, if the graph or drawing is going to be bound into a report (or published in a paper) that supplies the background information anyway, why clutter up the page with nonessential material?

We believe that every figure title should be no longer than necessary to make the figure readily comprehensible *in the medium where it is published*. Thus if you are going to use in your report or paper figures that were originally prepared to stand alone, you will do well to remove most of the title information that also appears in nearby text. Graphs that are to be published in important reports or papers will probably have to be redrawn anyway, for reasons discussed in Secs. 18.5.6 and 18.5.7.

18.5 Graphs and Curves

18.5.1 The Quick Look

Just as tables communicate some kinds of ideas more rapidly and more easily than exposition does, graphs and curves are often more effective and more efficient than either exposition or tables. The special virtue of graphs is that they present information very rapidly—at a glance— so that the viewer can grasp a number of values almost simultaneously. As a result, he is readily able to compare these values and to get an idea of their *relationships* with each other.

Consider this simple table of automobile fuel economy obtained from a proving-ground test:

Table 13.   Constant-speed Fuel Economy on Level Road
1958 Rumbler

Speed, Miles per Hour	Fuel Economy, Miles per Gallon	
	6-Cylinder Engine	8-Cylinder Engine
20	25.1	23.0
25	25.3	23.0
30	24.8	22.8
35	24.0	22.6
40	23.2	22.0
45	22.0	21.2
50	20.9	20.0
55	19.3	18.9
60	17.3	17.2
65	14.8	15.2
70	12.0	13.0
75	9.4	10.2
80	6.5	7.9

You can see that both engines consume more fuel as car speed increases; but at what speeds does this tendency become pronounced, and how do the two engines compare?   That is, "What is the shape of the curve?"

Now look at Fig. 8 on page 232.   You see immediately that (1) the falling off in fuel economy becomes rapidly more pronounced at higher speeds; and (2) the 6-cylinder engine is more economical than the 8 at low speeds but less economical from about 60 miles per hour up.

You can read the values of the fuel economy curves of Fig. 8 to perhaps ½ mile per gallon.   The scatter of the observed points indicates that closer readings are not warranted; and besides, smaller differences are not really significant.   Therefore, why not present the results of the fuel-economy test only in curve form, without any tabulation?

All of the graphical forms for presenting data show relationships; some of them stress the relationships, others simply the listing of facts. For our purposes graphs can be divided into three main categories:

(1) *The curve* is most useful in showing relationships among continuously varying phenomena; at the same time it presents facts.

Engineers and scientists use the curve more than any other kind of graph. Although the principles discussed in the rest of Sec. 18.5 pertain directly to curves, most of them may be applied also to bar charts.

(2) *The bar chart* presents information about discontinuous phe-

nomena or discrete quantities—the sort of information that is often simply listed in tables. The bar chart makes it particularly easy to *compare* data. It is a valuable tool that engineers could profitably use oftener than they do.

A special adaptation of the bar chart is the pictorial chart, in which quantities are represented not by the lengths of bars, but by the lengths of rows (and thus by the number) of little pictorial symbols each of which stands for a stated number of units. The pictorial chart is effective in presenting numerical data to laymen, who are not generally conversant with graphical representations. But scientists and engineers will not be baffled by bar-chart representation, and they may be annoyed by the naïveté and lack of precision of the pictorial chart. Therefore, when your audience is technically trained you will probably do better to use ordinary bar charts rather than pictorial charts.

(3) *The pie chart* is an effective and highly specialized device for showing just one thing—proportion, or percentage, of the whole. Although it is used in business reports more than in technical reports, the pie chart should not be overlooked by technical men.

18.5.2 Direction of Variables

According to a well-established convention, the independent variable is plotted horizontally, the dependent variable vertically (except that bar charts are sometimes constructed with the bars running horizontally). You should follow this convention if only because your readers will be momentarily confused if you do not. But besides, it is a convention that has a good, logical basis. We are primarily interested in values of the dependent variable, and it seems natural to express magnitude by height.

18.5.3 Scale Labels

Remember to furnish complete scale information along the sides or axes of every graph. Unless a curve is used to show only the rough shape of a relationship, each scale label contains two pieces of information: the name of the variable and the units in which it is measured.

These two pieces of information are best separated by a comma, thus:

Frequency, megacycles

Another acceptable method is to put the units in parenthesis, thus:

Height above sea level (feet)

The word *in* will serve as a separator, but it takes up additional space:

Current in amperes

Some people separate the name of the variable from the units by a dash:

Change of free energy—calories

But because the dash may occasionally be taken for a minus sign, you should get in the habit of avoiding this notation.

You have probably seen scales labeled with multipliers, like this:

Force, lb × 1000

or

Force, lb ÷ 1000

Such multipliers do save space by eliminating a lot of zeros from the numbers along the axes, but they result in at least momentary ambiguity. The reader wonders, "Have these numbers *been* multiplied (or divided) by a thousand, or am I *supposed to* multiply them (or divide them) by a thousand?" His knowledge of the subject under discussion will probably enable him to answer the question after a little thought, but you should not put him to this trouble. Better, express your multiplier in an unambiguous way:

Force, thousands of lb

18.5.4 Choice of Scale

(1) *Rational Scale*

Always choose a rational scale—that is, one that neither underemphasizes nor overemphasizes the importance of the changes you are depicting. For instance, the curve of Fig. 2 gives the impression that the octane number of commercial gasolines increased very rapidly but sporadically in the decade between 1930 and 1940. The same data plotted to different scales in Fig. 3 seem to indicate that the improvement was gradual but steady. A truer representation would be given by scales somewhere between the two used in these figures.

There is no formula for the choice of rational scales. You simply have to look at the slope of your curve and consider whether it seems to give an accurate impression of the idea you are trying to convey.

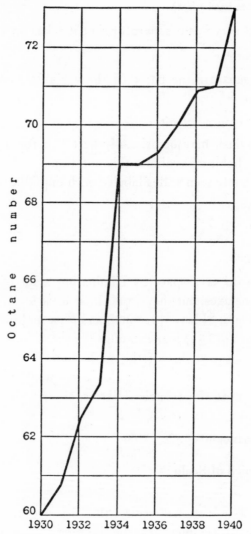

Fig. 2. Trend in motor method octane number of regular gasoline
(Changes overemphasized)

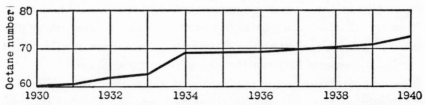

Fig. 3. Trend in motor method octane number of regular gasoline
(Changes underemphasized)

(2) *Values for Scale*

For ordinary decimal graph paper (each main division divided into 10 subdivisions) the value of each main division should be restricted to 1, 2, or 5 and their multiples by any power of 10. Thus you can let each main division represent 0.01 or 1 or 100 or 1,000,000; 0.2 or 2 or 200; 0.005 or 5 or 5000; and so on.

Points plotted according to this rather arbitrary-sounding rule can be read almost by inspection. For instance, see how quickly you can read the points in Fig. 4.

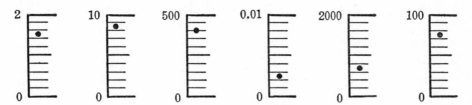

Fig. 4. Points plotted to permissible scales

But in a misguided effort to make the curve look pretty, or to fill up the paper, some people assign other values to the main divisions of decimal graph paper. Now try to read the points of Fig. 5 rapidly.

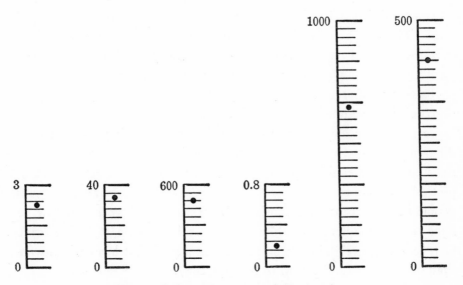

Fig. 5. Points plotted to prohibited scales

And remember that these scales will not only bother your reader, but will also slow you down while you are doing the plotting. Better stick to the "permissible" scales.

18.5.5 Bold Curves

When you plot a curve on commercial graph paper—which is usually printed in a shade of red or green—the curve is clearly distinguished from the lines of the grid by color separation. But when this sheet is reproduced in one color by Ozalid or any other photographic process, color difference no longer separates the curve from the grid, and they tend to become confused, as shown in Fig. 6.

If you plan to make one-color prints from your graphs (as is done for practically all technical reports), *you should make the curves at least 3 times as thick as the thickest grid lines.* In Fig. 7 the curves of Fig. 6 have been made considerably thicker; notice how they stand out from the grid background.

There is one exception to this rule: if you are plotting a *working* curve, such as a calibration curve, from which values must be read precisely, you will probably have to use a fine line and hope that it will never be confused with the grid lines.

18.5.6 Coarse Grid

The commercial graph paper most often used has 20 divisions to the inch. This fine grid is often confusing; it is usually unwarranted; and it is always hard on the eyes (see Figs. 6 and 7). Whenever you prepare a graph for publication in a report or paper, by all means *use the coarsest grid that will permit values to be read with the appropriate precision.* Sometimes you can omit the grid entirely.

Certainly you should not use a grid that makes it possible to read differences that are smaller than the experimental error or that are so small as to be meaningless. For instance, we have seen octane numbers plotted on a grid whose smallest division represented 0.05 number. Now, octane numbers cannot be consistently measured to less than 0.5 or perhaps 0.2, and differences of less than 0.5 have little real significance. Octane numbers should not be plotted on a grid that has divisions finer than 0.5 (which can be read to perhaps 0.2).

You can avoid the fine grid in several ways: (1) You can use commercial graph paper with 1, 2, or 10 divisions to the inch. (2) You can use commercial graph paper with a grid printed in blue ink, which will not be reproduced on prints made from this paper. Before the prints are run, you can reinforce with India ink those grid lines that are to appear on the final copy. (3) Even if you prefer to do your preliminary plotting on ordinary 20-to-the-inch graph paper, you can trace your final copy on plain tracing paper, inking in only the wanted grid lines. Fig. 8 is a traced copy of Fig. 6. Notice that it is very much easier on the eyes than the versions with fine grids; yet it permits the fuel economy to be read to ½ mile per gallon, the greatest precision warranted by the nature of the data.

18.5.7 No Lettering on Grid

Try to avoid having any lettering superimposed on the grid lines. In Fig. 6 the lettering, both of the scales and the internal labels, is typed right on the grid. Color separation made it reasonably legible on the original sheet. But on this one-color reproduction, confusion with the grid lines makes the lettering difficult to read.

In Fig. 7 the scales are placed in the clear margin outside of the grid area, and clear spaces have been provided within the grid area for the internal labels. The lettering is much more easily legible than in Fig. 6. (But see the caution about binding margin in Sec. 16.9.)

Clear areas for lettering may be provided in several ways, depending on the kind of paper and the method of reproduction to be used:

(1) If a commercial graph sheet is to be reproduced by photolithography or photography (but not by direct printing), you can do your lettering on strips of white paper and paste them over the grid.

(2) If a commercial graph sheet is to be reproduced by direct printing, you can do your plotting and lettering on the back of the paper, and then with a blade scrape away the grid from behind the lettering.

(3) If you are tracing your curve sheet on plain paper—no matter how it is going to be reproduced—you can simply omit the grid lines wherever there is lettering inside the grid area; see Fig. 8.

To comply with the principles of this section and the preceding one, you should probably trace on plain paper most curves that are going to be published in any but very informal reports.

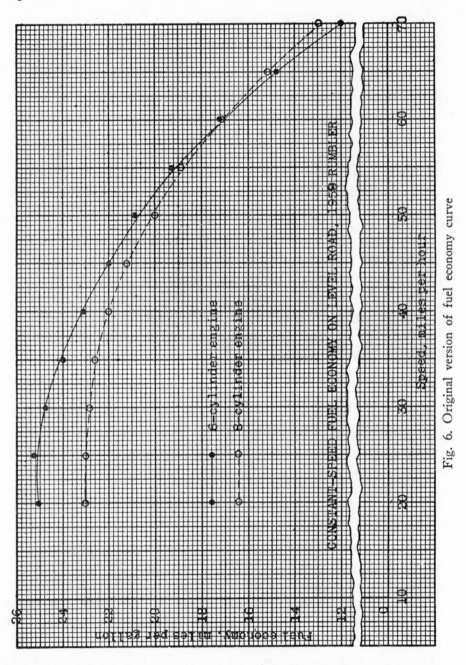

Fig. 6. Original version of fuel economy curve

NOTE: So that they would fit the pages of this book without being reduced or scaled down, Fig. 6 and its revised versions (Figs. 7, 8, 15, and 16) have been condensed. That is, part of the vertical scale has been removed (see Sec. 18.5.9), and the curves have been cut off at 70

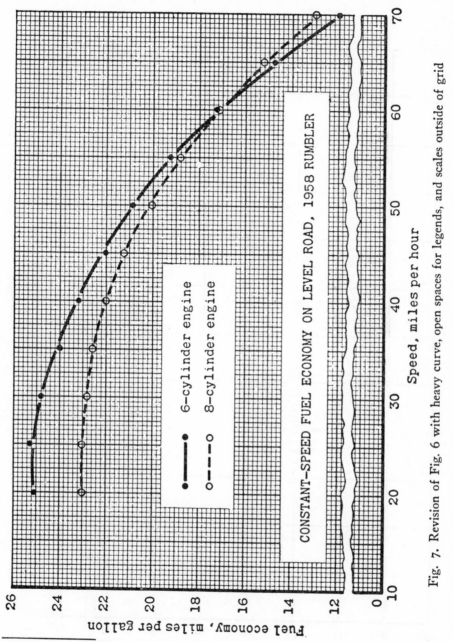

Fig. 7. Revision of Fig. 6 with heavy curve, open spaces for legends, and scales outside of grid

miles per hour. In reality, all of these curves would be plotted on 8½ x 11-inch paper; the vertical scales would run from 0 through 26 miles per gallon without a break; and the horizontal scales and the curves would be extended to 80 miles per hour.

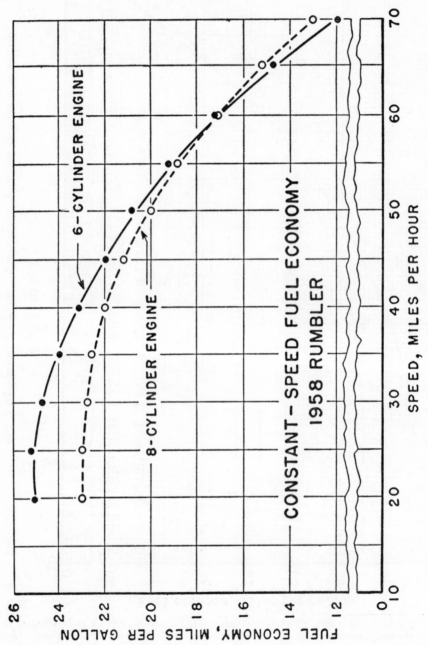

Fig. 8. Revision of Fig. 7 with only major grid lines traced, key replaced by labels

18.5.8 Label for Each Curve

Whenever more than one curve is plotted on one set of coordinates, it must be possible (1) to distinguish the curves and (2) to identify them. As shown in Figs. 6 and 7, the curves are usually distinguished by the use of differing symbols and lines. They are often identified by a *key* like the one in these two figures.

With this device the identification process is a double one, involving excursions of the eyes back and forth between the key and the curves in order to connect the names with the codes. A more direct method for identifying the curves—individual labels—is illustrated in Fig. 8. Individual labels are much more helpful than a key. You should use them unless physical complications on the curve sheet prevent.

18.5.9 Suppressed Zero

When the scale of the independent variable starts at any value above zero, it is said to have a *suppressed zero*. Because the function of graphs is to present information at a glance, the suppressed zero can be very misleading. Look at this bar chart (Fig. 9) from the annual report of a corporation.

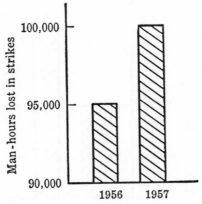

Fig. 9. Difference exaggerated by suppressed zero

The quick comparison so easy with a bar chart gives you the impression that the corporation lost twice as many hours in strikes in 1957 as it did in 1956. A more careful examination reveals that the 1957 loss was only about 5 percent greater than the 1956 loss.

The suppressed zero is sometimes used with the intention of misleading. This is an inherently dishonest practice.

But there is often a perfectly good justification for the suppressed zero. If the vertical scale of Fig. 9 had been brought down to zero, the graph would have looked like Fig. 10.

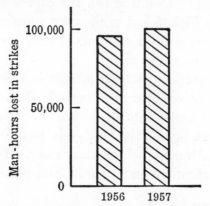

Fig. 10. Significant difference obscured

Now a significant difference—5000 man-hours—is hardly discernible. It is legitimate to suppress the zero so that a difference can be read; but whenever you do so, be sure to announce the fact plainly. Fig. 11 illustrates one way of indicating a suppressed zero.

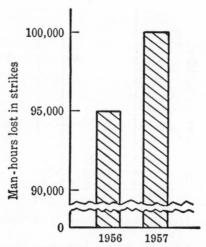

Fig. 11. Suppressed zero indicated

It is not necessary to call attention to the suppressed zero when you are representing arbitrary units, such as degrees of temperature or octane numbers (see Figs. 2 and 3), in which the zero has no real significance.

18.6 Other Forms of Visual Presentation

Information may be transmitted by numerous visual means besides graphs and curves. Drawings, diagrams, schematics, photographs, exploded views—even models—all make their contribution to the efficient communication of ideas.

These aids are usually produced by specialists, and a full discussion of them is outside the scope of this book. But we do want to enlarge upon the plea for simplicity voiced in Sec. 18.4.1.

Fig. 12 is the *working drawing,* or *assembly drawing,* of a conventional superheterodyne radio receiving set. If you are a radio technician, you can assemble a set from this drawing, and you can undoubtedly understand how it works. But if you are not a radio technician or an electrical engineer, how much does this drawing tell you about the essential nature and function of the various elements of the set and their relationships with each other?

Now consider Fig. 13, a *schematic diagram* of the same receiving set. The elimination of many of the details—or lines—of the working drawing clarifies the general scheme of the apparatus; but still, unless you are used to reading circuit schematics you probably cannot tell how the set works.

Finally, look at Fig. 14, a *block diagram* of the radio set. Here the main elements are represented simply by blocks, and their *logical relationships* with each other are indicated by arrows. Notice how very quickly you can grasp the basic scheme of the set. A block diagram like this conveys intelligible information even to a layman; and to a technical man it describes fundamental arrangements more rapidly and more easily than any other means.

A consideration of these figures leads to an important general rule: *Always use the simplest—or least detailed—form of representation that still supplies those details needed for your immediate purposes.*

Quite often you will have occasion to provide several representations of an idea or an apparatus at increasing levels of detail. Even though you must finally supply complete working drawings, you may start out by presenting the basic, over-all scheme in a simple block diagram or flow diagram. Between this and the final drawing may be one or more diagrams on intermediate levels.

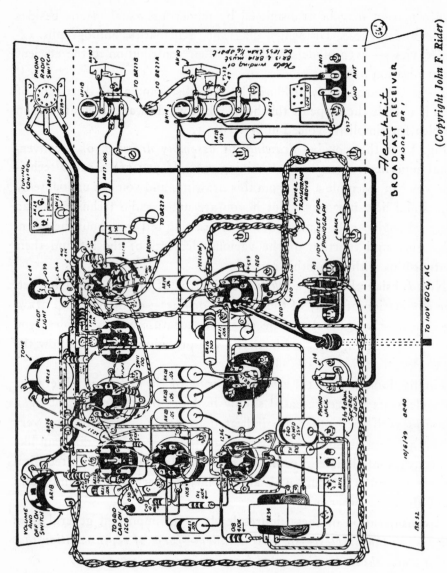

Fig. 12. Assembly drawing of broadcast receiver

(Copyright John F. Rider)

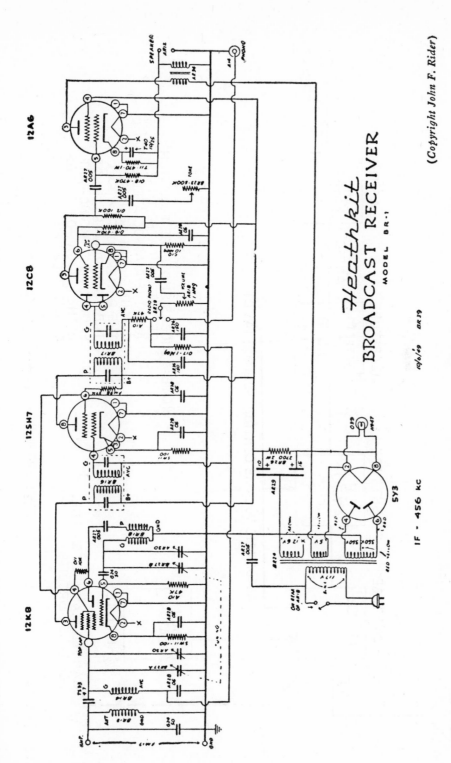

Heathkit
BROADCAST RECEIVER
MODEL BR-1

IF - 456 KC

Fig. 13. Schematic diagram of broadcast receiver

(Copyright John F. Rider)

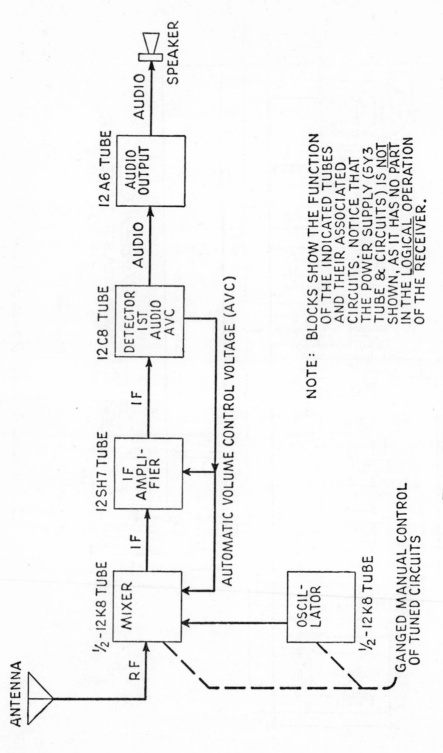

ANTENNA

RF

½-12K8 TUBE
MIXER

IF

12SH7 TUBE
IF AMPLI-FIER

IF

12C8 TUBE
DETECTOR
IST AUDIO
AVC

AUDIO

12A6 TUBE
AUDIO OUTPUT

AUDIO

SPEAKER

AUTOMATIC VOLUME CONTROL VOLTAGE (AVC)

½-12K8 TUBE
OSCIL-LATOR

GANGED MANUAL CONTROL OF TUNED CIRCUITS

NOTE: BLOCKS SHOW THE FUNCTION OF THE INDICATED TUBES AND THEIR ASSOCIATED CIRCUITS. NOTICE THAT THE POWER SUPPLY (5Y3 TUBE & CIRCUITS) IS NOT SHOWN, AS IT HAS NO PART IN THE LOGICAL OPERATION OF THE RECEIVER.

Fig. 14. Block diagram of broadcast receiver

18.7 Slides

18.7.1 Simplicity

Any of the visual aids, including tables, may be made into lantern slides to accompany oral presentation of papers and reports (see Chapter 11). When a speaker uses a slide to help him communicate his ideas to an audience, he seldom stops talking while the slide is on the screen. If a slide requires extended study, the listener has the choice of comprehending the slide or listening to the speaker. He cannot do both.

We have stressed the importance of simplicity in all the visual aids; but in slides it is doubly important. Unless a slide presents information at a glance, it defeats its own purpose. A slide should have on it no detail that is not needed, no data that is not referred to in the talk. Every superfluous line should be removed; every line that remains should be clear, and the important lines such as curves should be extra bold.

These general ideas have been codified into some useful specific rules by the professional societies, at whose meetings so many slides are thrown upon the screen. In its helpful booklet *Hints to Authors,* the American Chemical Society says that each slide should be limited to the presentation of one idea; that a slide should contain not more than 20 words, and preferably not more than 15; and that a table should have no more than 25 or 30 data.

18.7.2 The 1/40 Rule

In a bulletin on lantern slides, the Society of Automotive Engineers propounds the highly valuable rule that *no letter or figure shall be less than ¼₀ the vertical height of the copy.* Main titles and other important words can of course be proportionately larger. Application of this rule results in lettering that shocks most draftsmen on first acquaintance; but it has been a godsend to the back rows of technical-society audiences.

The ¼₀ rule assumes that the height of the copy is its limiting dimension. If the ratio of width to height is greater than the 3/2.25 of the standard lantern slide, then the width becomes the limiting dimension. In this event, the hypothetical height is 2.25/3 of the actual width, and the smallest characters should be at least ¼₀ of this hypothetical height.

If you draw your slides horizontally on 8½ x 11-inch paper so as to fill up most of the sheet, the *smallest* characters should be made with a 175-size (0.175-inch) Leroy or Wrico guide. It is a good idea to standardize on $8\frac{1}{2}$ x 11-inch paper for slide drawings. This practice will produce slides of uniform appearance; and any slide that cannot be conveniently drawn on a sheet of this size very probably has too much on it.

The empirical $\frac{1}{40}$ rule leads to an important corollary: *No two lines that are to be resolved, or seen as being separate, shall be closer together than $\frac{1}{80}$ the height (or hypothetical height) of the copy.*

18.7.3 Special Copy for Slides

If you make your slides, or have them made, according to the principles of Secs. 18.7.1 and 18.7.2, you will find that you cannot simply photograph the figures you have prepared for publication. You will practically always have to make up copy expressly for the slides. The curves of Fig. 8 are shown in Fig. 15 redrawn in a slide version. Notice the larger letters. (Remember that this graph has been condensed. To preserve the $\frac{1}{40}$ relationship, the smallest letters have been made with a 120 Leroy guide. If the figure had not been condensed from $8\frac{1}{2}$ x 11 inches, the smallest letters would be the 175 size.) Notice also the shortened captions, the bolder curves, the substitution of stubs for the grid. A slide made from this copy will be easily legible even in the last row of a smoke-filled auditorium.

On the other hand, if you start out by preparing copy for the slides, you can use this same material for the published version of a talk. It will look bold and black, but it will be legible and neat when it is reduced to one-column size.

18.7.4 Negative Slides

When an ordinary positive image of a drawing or graph is projected, most of the screen is very intensely illuminated. The brilliant screen in the otherwise dark room is at least unpleasant to look at; it can cause objectionable eyestrain.

The use of negative slides, which are becoming increasingly popular, avoids this undesirable effect. In the preparation of a negative slide the copy is photographed from a distance that makes the image just fit the standard slide mask opening. Then the negative is simply mounted between two slide cover glasses. (As explained in Sec. 18.7.5, drawings for negative slides should be specially prepared.)

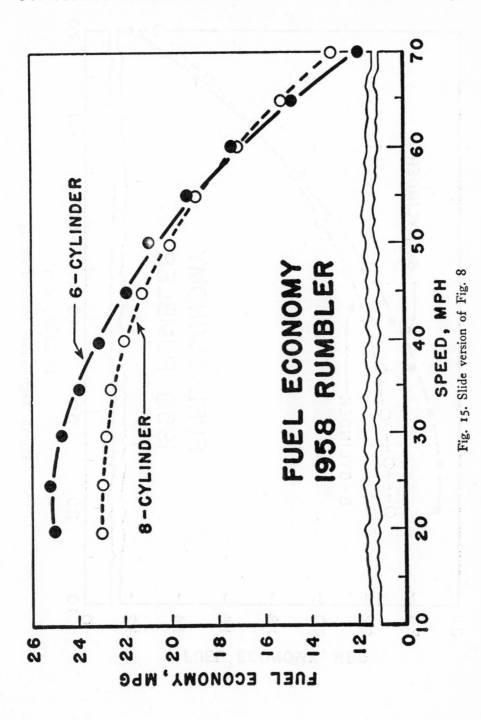

Fig. 15. Slide version of Fig. 8

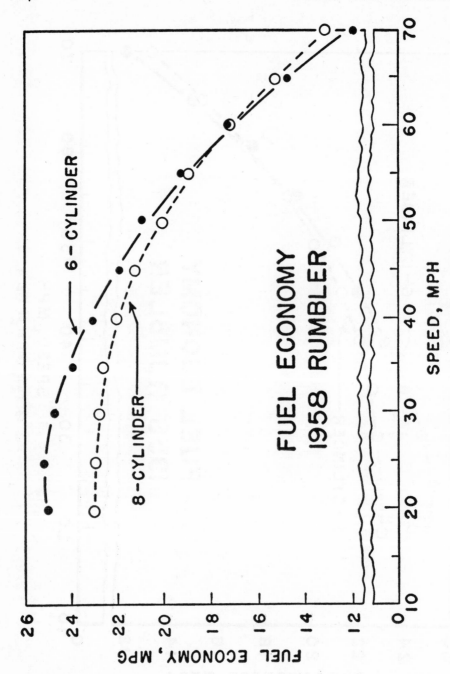

FUEL ECONOMY
1958 RUMBLER

6 – CYLINDER

8 – CYLINDER

FUEL ECONOMY, MPG

SPEED, MPH

Fig. 16. Negative slide version of Fig. 15

The resulting image consists of bright lines on a dark background. The screen does not glare unpleasantly.

Negative slides lend themselves to the use of color. The transparent lines of the image can be tinted with water colors, so that different parts of a drawing or different curves on a graph can be easily distinguished. If the color runs over onto adjacent dark background, no harm is done.

Negative slides should not be shown in a projector without forced ventilation.

18.7.5 Pen Size

Because of the brilliant illumination of the projector, the projected image of a slide is subject to halation—that is, bright parts of the image tend to bleed over into dark parts. As a result, the dark lines on a positive slide tend to look thinner than they are, while the bright lines on a negative slide tend to look thicker. This effect is especially noticeable in the lettering.

Therefore it is a good idea to make all the lines in a positive slide a little heavier than normal. Leroy or Wrico lettering may be done with a pen one or two sizes heavier than the standard for each letter size.

On the other hand, lines on the copy for a negative slide should be a little finer than normal, *and should be kept well separated.* To avoid "filling up" and blurring of the lettering, the pen should be one or two sizes lighter than standard. The copy for a positive slide (Fig. 15) has been redrawn for a negative slide in Fig. 16.

19. IN CONCLUSION

Whenever you have a technical reporting job to do, remember:

(1) Be as clear and as brief as you can.

(2) Design your material for your intended audience.

(3) Start with a statement of the purpose and the basic nature of the whole; then fill in the details. Orient your readers thoroughly.

(4) Don't bury important ideas under a mass of details. Eliminate unimportant details or get them out of the way in an appendix.

(5) Use headings and subheadings liberally.

(6) Be consistent.

(7) Be specific.

(8) Outline before you start writing.

(9) After you have completed a draft, set it aside as long as possible before you undertake the job of revision and polishing.

(10) Proofread your final copy carefully, and correct all errors, big or little.

(11) Try to tailor the outline of every report to fit its specific subject and its specific purpose.

(12) Unless the method you use in an investigation is more important than the results of the investigation, subordinate the description of

the method to the presentation and discussion of the results. Provide only as much information about method as your readers will need.

(13) To save repetition, try to combine the presentation and discussion of results.

(14) Provide an *independent* summary at the beginning of every formal report and of every informal report that will be helped by one. Whenever possible, make your summaries and abstracts informative rather than simply descriptive.

(15) Do not be afraid to draw conclusions and make recommendations if you have been authorized to and if the data warrant them.

(16) Put into the appendix any material that needs to be included in the report but that is not an integral part of the main message. Key every section of the appendix to the text by a specific reference.

(17) For any report of more than three or four pages, provide a table of contents that will serve as an outline of the report.

(18) Be sure that your thesis subject requires some real research on your part.

(19) Save the time of other people by preparing adequate interview material and questionnaires.

(20) Write clearly and simply, using short, plain, concrete words. Eliminate unnecessary words. Avoid involved constructions, indirect expressions. Watch out for sentences that are too long, but try to vary the length of your sentences.

(21) Write grammatically. Watch out especially for vague pronouns, dangling modifiers.

(22) Spell correctly.

(23) Punctuate properly, as a help to your readers. Test your punctuation by reading aloud; a drop in your voice or a pause usually indicates the need for a comma (or a heavier mark). In particular, do not omit the comma (a) before the conjunction in a compound sentence, (b) around the nonrestrictive modifier, (c) before the conjunction in a series. Hyphenate compound adjectives that precede their nouns.

(24) Be sure your readers will know the meaning of any abbreviations you use. In scientific and technical abbreviations: (a) omit periods unless the abbreviation forms a word; (b) omit capitals unless the word abbreviated is a proper noun; (c) use the same abbreviation for singular and plural.

(25) Use Arabic numerals freely.

(26) Allow at least 1¼ inches margin on the left edge of any sheet that is going to be bound into standard report covers.

(27) Use tables, graphs, and diagrams liberally. Key every one of them to the text by an early reference. Keep them simple and uncluttered.

(28) Choose a rational scale for every graph, and mark it plainly, with units. Use the coarsest grid that will permit readings to the desired precision. Make all curves as bold as possible.

(29) When you have to deliver a talk, prepare a simple version of your material, concentrating on a full, clear presentation of only the important points. Provide frequent recapitulations. Do not memorize your speech, and do not read it unless you must. Speak slowly, clearly, and loud. Modulate your voice. Look at your audience. Don't move around unnecessarily, and be on guard against nervous mannerisms. Relax.

20. APPENDIX

20.1 Abbreviations for Scientific and Engineering Terms (from American Standards Association Publication Z10.1–1941)

These forms are recommended for readers whose familiarity with the terms used makes possible a maximum of abbreviations. For other classes of readers editors may wish to use less contracted combinations made up from this list. For example, the list gives the abbreviation of the term "feet per second" as "fps." To some readers "ft per sec" will be more easily understood.

absolute ....abs	avoirdupois ....avdp
acre ....spell out	azimuth ....az or α
acre-foot ....acre-ft	
air horsepower ....air hp	barometer ....bar.
alternating-current (as adjective) ...a-c	barrel ....bbl
ampere ....amp	Baumé ....Bé
ampere-hour ....amp-hr	boiler pressure..............spell out
amplitude, an elliptic function .....am.	boiling point ....bp
Angstrom unit ....A	brake horsepower ....bhp
antilogarithm ....antilog	brake horsepower-hour ....bhp-hr
atmosphere ....atm	Brinell hardness number ....Bhn
atomic weight ....at. wt	British thermal unit [1] ....Btu or B
average ....avg	bushel ....bu

[1] Abbreviation recommended by the A.S.M.E. Power Test Codes Committee. B = 1 Btu, kB = 1000 Btu, mB = 1,000,000 Btu. The A.S.H.&V.E. recommends the use of Mb = 1000 Btu and Mbh = 1000 Btu per hr.

calorie ....cal

candle c

candle-hour ....c-hr

candlepower ....cp

cent ....c or ¢

center to center ....c to c

centigram ....cg

centiliter cl

centimeter ....cm

centimeter-gram-second (system) ...cgs

chemical ....chem

chemically pure ....cp

circular ....cir

circular mils ....cir mils

coefficient ....coef

cologarithm ....colog

concentrate ....conc

conductivity ....cond

constant ....const

cosecant ....csc

cosine ....cos

cosine of the amplitude,
    an elliptic function ....cn

cotangent ....cot

coulomb ....spell out

counter electromotive force ......cemf

cubic ....cu

cubic centimeter ....cu cm, cm³ (liquid,
    meaning milliliter, ml)

cubic foot ....cu ft

cubic feet per minute ....cfm

cubic feet per second ....cfs

cubic inch ....cu in.

cubic meter .... cu m or m³

cubic micron ....cu μ or cu mu or μ³

cubic millimeter ....cu mm or mm³

cubic yard ....cu yd

current density ....spell out

cycles per second ....spell out or c

cylinder ....cyl

decibel ....db

degree [2] ....deg or °

degree centigrade C

degree Fahrenheit ....F

degree Kelvin ....K

degree Réaumur ....R

delta amplitude, an elliptic function .dn

diameter ....diam

direct-current (as adjective) ......d-c

dollar ....$

dozen ....doz

dram ....dr

efficiency ....eff

electric ....elec

electromotive force ....emf

elevation ....el

equation ....eq

external ....ext

farad ....spell out or f

feet per minute ....fpm

feet per second ....fps

fluid ....fl

foot ....ft

foot-candle ....ft-c

foot-Lambert ....ft-L

foot-pound ....ft-lb

foot-pound-second (system) ....fps

foot-second (see cubic feet per second)

free on board ....fob

freezing point ....fp

frequency ....spell out

fusion point ....fnp

gallon ....gal

gallons per minute..............gpm

gallons per second ....gps

grain ....spell out

gram ....g

gram-calorie ....g-cal

[2] There are circumstances under which one or the other of these forms is preferred. In general the sign ° is used where space conditions make it necessary, as in tabular matter, and when abbreviations are cumbersome, as in some angular measurements, i.e., 59° 23′ 42″. In the interest of simplicity and clarity the Committee has recommended that the abbreviation for the temperature scale, F, C, K, etc., always be included in expressions for numerical temperatures, but, wherever feasible, the abbreviation for "degree" be omitted; as 69 F.

greatest common divisor ....gcd

haversine ....hav
henry ....h
high-pressure (adjective) ....h-p
horsepower ....hp
horsepower-hour ....hp-hr
hour ....hr
hour (in astronomical tables) ....h
hundred C
hundredweight (112 lb).........cwt
hyperbolic cosine ....cosh
hyperbolic sine ....sinh
hyperbolic tangent ....tanh

inch ....in.
inch-pound ....in-lb
inches per second ....ips
indicated horsepower ....ihp
indicated horsepower-hour ......ihp-hr
inside diameter ....ID
intermediate-pressure (adjective) ...i-p
internal ....int

joule ....j

kilocalorie ....kcal
kilocycles per second ....kc
kilogram ....kg
kilogram-calorie ....kg-cal
kilogram-meter ....kg-m
kilograms per cubic meter .. kg per cu m
    or kg/m^3
kilograms per second ....kgps
kiloliter ....kl
kilometer ....km
kilometers per second ....kmps
kilovolt ....kv
kilovolt-ampere ....kva
kilowatt ....kw
kilowatthour ....kwhr

lambert L
latitude ....lat or ϕ
least common multiple ....lcm
linear foot ....lin ft
liquid ....liq

liter l
logarithm (common) ....log
logarithm (natural) ....$\log_e$ or ln
longitude ....long. or λ
low-pressure (as adjective) ....l-p
lumen l
lumen-hour ....l-hr
lumens per watt ....lpw

mass ....spell out
mathematics (ical) ....math
maximum ....max
mean effective pressure ....mep
mean horizontal candlepower ....mhcp
megacycle ....spell out
megohm ....spell out
melting point ....mp
meter ....m
meter-kilogram ....m-kg
mho ....spell out
microampere ....μa or mu a
microfarad ....μf
microinch ....μin.
micromicrofarad ....$\mu\mu$f
micromicron ....$\mu\mu$ or mu mu
micron ....μ or mu
microvolt ....μv
microwatt ....μw or mu w
mile ....spell out
miles per hour ....mph
miles per hour per second ......mphps
milliampere ....ma
milligram ....mg
millihenry ....mh
millilambert ....mL
milliliter ....ml
millimeter ....mm
millimicron ....$m\mu$ or m mu
million ....spell out
million gallons per day.........mgd
millivolt ....mv
minimum ....min
minute ....min
minute (angular measure) ....'
minute (time) (in astronomical
    tables) ....m
mole ....spell out

molecular weight ....mol. wt
month ....spell out

National Electrical Code ....NEC

ohm ....spell out or Ω
ohm-centimeter ....ohm-cm
ounce ....oz
ounce-foot ....oz-ft
ounce-inch ....oz-in.
outside diameter ....OD

parts per million ....ppm
peck ....pk
penny (pence) ....d
pennyweight ....dwt
per ....(See Sec. 13.1.2)
pint ....pt
potential ....spell out
potential difference ....spell out
pound ....lb
pound-foot ....lb-ft
pound-inch ....lb-in.
pound sterling ....£
pounds per brake horse-
    power-hour ....lb per bhp-hr
pounds per cubic foot ......lb per cu ft
pounds per square foot ....psf
pounds per square inch ....psi
pounds per square inch absolute ...psia
power factor ....spell out or pf

quart ....qt

radian ....spell out
reactive kilovolt-ampere ....kvar
reactive volt-ampere ....var
revolutions per minute ....rpm
revolutions per second ....rps
rod ....spell out
root mean square ....rms

secant ....sec
second ....sec

second (angular measure) ...."
second-foot (see cubic feet per second)
second (time) (in astronomical
    tables) ....s
shaft horsepower ....shp
sine ....sin
sine of the amplitude,
    an elliptic function ....sn
specific gravity ....sp gr
specific heat ....sp ht
spherical candle power ....scp
square ....sq
square centimeter ....sq cm or cm^2
square foot ....sq ft
square inch ....sq in.
square kilometer ....sq km or km^2
square meter ....sq m or m^2
square micron ......sq μ or sq mu or μ^2
square millimeter ......sq mm or mm^2
square root of mean square ....rms
standard ....std

tangent ....tan
temperature ....temp
tensile strength ....ts
thousand ....M
thousand foot-pounds ....kip-ft
thousand pound ....kip
ton ....spell out
ton-mile ....spell out
versed sine ....vers
volt v
volt-ampere ....va
volt-coulomb ....spell out

watt ....w
watthour ....whr
watts per candle ....wpc
week ....spell out
weight ....wt

yard ....yd
year ....yr

20.2 Specimen Reports

Section 20.2 contains specimen reports and letters that illustrate the ideas discussed in *Technical Reporting*. Remember that these are simply examples from a wide choice of acceptable forms.

The originals of all these specimens were typed on 8½ x 11-inch paper. The condensation required to make them fit the pages of this book has resulted in some crowding, but the specimens will serve their illustrative purpose.

Reports and letters of this kind are usually typed on only one side of the paper. This practice has been largely followed here: most of the specimen material appears on the right-hand pages only. On the facing left-hand pages are pertinent remarks and comments.

20.2.1 Specimen Memo Report

This memo report was written to make the results of an investigation available to a number of engineers working on different parts of an extensive development program. Although it is less than four pages long, it contains many of the features of organization usually associated with the formal report. But notice that the text begins on the front page, right under the heading.

Brief as it is, the foreword provides ample background and orientation information for the readers to whom this report is addressed.

The conclusions on page 1 enable the busy reader to get the important useful information—the "action" information—from this report without going further.

Memo Report E-76

XYZ Computer Project
Massachusetts Institute of Technology
Cambridge, Massachusetts

SUBJECT: COUPLING BETWEEN FLIP-FLOP AND GATE TUBE
To: All Project Engineers
From: N. Daggett
Date: February 7, 1952

Foreword

In the development of the basic circuits for the high-speed electronic digital computer being designed by this Project, three questions have arisen repeatedly: (1) whether a delay element is necessary between a gate tube and a flip-flop triggered at the cathode by the same input pulse; (2) whether there is danger that feedback from the suppressor grid of the gate tube will cause unwanted triggering of the gate tube; and (3) what size coupling condenser should be used between flip-flop and gate tube. This report describes the results of an investigation undertaken to supply generally applicable answers to these questions.

Conclusions

1. Delay Element

The improved suppressor-control characteristic of the new gate tube (SR-1030) makes a delay element unnecessary between flip-flop and gate tube.

2. Unwanted Triggering

With the suppressor-grid waveform of the gate tube clamped to ground, there is no danger that feedback will cause unwanted triggering.

3. Coupling Condenser

As long as the flip-flop is supplied with restorer pulses, the coupling condenser between flip-flop and gate tube may be as large as desired; 560 $\mu\mu$f seems to be the minimum allowable for satisfactory gating.

The original report was reproduced by the hectograph process (see Sec. 16.11.1). When the master was being typed, spaces were left for the two sketches. Then they were drawn on the master with an ordinary pencil. Appearing right with the text that they illustrate, they are convenient for the reader.

Notice that each of the sketches comes after the reference to it in the text. When you first see the sketch, you know what it is about, why it is in the report, and how it fits into the text.

Discussion of Work

        1. Delay Element

        Clock pulses were applied simultaneously to a gate tube and a flip-flop connected in the circuit of Fig. 1.

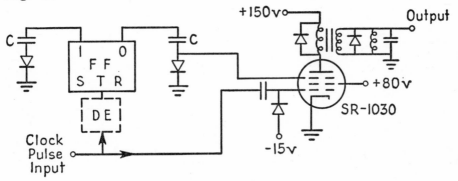

Fig. 1. Test circuit

        Typical waveforms of the output and the suppressor grid of the gate tube are shown in Fig. 2.

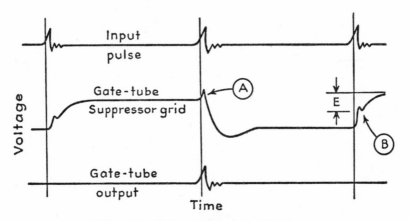

Fig. 2. Gate-tube waveforms

        With no delay, the small positive pip at A on the suppressor-grid waveform (caused by plate-to-cathode capacitance in the flip-flop) occurs at the instant the input pulse arrives at the control grid of the gate tube.

The discussion furnishes support for the conclusions stated on the first page of the report. In its logical development, it again arrives at the same conclusions.

Notice that descriptions, results, and discussion of the work done are integrated in each subsection.

It therefore causes a gate output somewhat greater than
occurs when the trigger to the flip-flop is delayed. Because both tubes of the flip-flop are held cut off by the
trigger at the cathode, the fall after the point A does
not cause any appreciable attenuation of the gate output
pulse.

The most critical part of the operation occurs
at B on the suppressor-grid waveform. Here a positive pip
from the incoming trigger is again superposed on the rise
of the flip-flop plate. If the voltage E (Fig. 2) becomes
less than the cutoff voltage of the suppressor grid, the
unwanted input pulse begins to appear at the gate-tube
output.

Clock pulses of 0.05 and 0.1 microsecond were
tried at both 1 and 2 megacycles with no delay, and gating
was uniformly satisfactory. The voltage E was approximately twice the cutoff voltage of the C-5104 gate tube.

The only result of inserting a 0.1-microsecond
delay line between input trigger and flip-flop was a
slight decrease in the amplitude of the output pulse (because the previously mentioned pip on the suppressor-grid
waveform no longer coincides with the input pulse).

2. Unwanted Triggering

To study the possibility that the flip-flop
would be triggered by feedback from the gate-tube suppressor grid, clock pulses were applied to the gate with
no trigger to the flip-flop. With the flip-flop in its
most unfavorable position, no triggering occurred regardless of the amplitude of the input pulses or of the amount
of external capacitance connected from the suppressor grid
to the plate of the gate tube.

Next a 0.5-microsecond delay line was inserted
between the input (1-megacycle clock pulses) and the flip-
flop. If any undesired triggering occurred, the flip-flop
waveforms would show it. There was no such triggering,
even when enough capacitance was added between suppressor
grid and plate to distort the output waveform of the gate
tube.

3. Coupling Condenser

The flip-flop coupling condensers (C in Fig. 1) were raised to values as high as 0.1 μf. In all cases the flip-flop started readily on restorer pulses regardless of the state of the flip-flop. With 560-$\mu\mu$f coupling condensers and with the crystals shunted by 0.1-megohm resistors, the voltage at the suppressor grid decayed about 10 percent during the interval between restorer pulses.

20.2.2 Specimen Memorandum

This memorandum, like the preceding report, uses one of the acceptable heading forms. This heading enables you to identify the report and its subject quickly and easily.

Although it is less than a page long, this memorandum is clarified by its two subheads and its two tabulated items.

Computer Applications Project
Massachusetts Institute of Technology
Cambridge, Massachusetts

SUBJECT: HEADINGS AND NUMBERS FOR 2345 REPORTS
To: All Secretaries; Applications Group
From: J. S. Underwood
Date: May 4, 1952

Headings

As shown above, headings for informal reports on the
Computer Applications Project, CID Project 2345, will
differ in two respects from the regular XYZ Computer
Project headings:

1. The number 2345 will replace the number 1234
   in the upper left corner.
2. The first line of the title will read Computer Applications Project instead of XYZ
   Computer Project.

Numbers

Reports on the Computer Applications Project will be
issued in the appropriate R-, E-, and A-series, but their
numbers will be in a block separate from those of the XYZ
Computer Project, starting with No. 2000. Numbers will be
assigned by the Librarian according to the usual procedure.

Signed _J. S. Underwood_____
                J. S. Underwood

Approved _L. S. Thurston_____
                L. S. Thurston

JSU:jz

20.2.3 Specimen Service Report in Memo Form

This memo is an example of a trip report. It originated in a government office and was used only for internal circulation. It is a good example of how a specific agency has adapted certain principles of reporting to a basic situation occurring over and over again.

The first page only has been reproduced here, as the minutes referred to in 4 would take up too much space. However, by looking over the section on results, you can tell what business was taken up, just as the original reader was able to.

OFFICE MEMORANDUM   LUMMUS ARSENAL
                                           10 August 1958

TO: Chief, National Commercial Division
        THRU: Mr. A. M. Farrar

FROM: Henry S. Bowers, Publications Section
        Industrial Engineering Branch

SUBJECT: Report of Travel

PLACE VISITED AND DATE:

        Ordnance Weapons Command, Red Island Arsenal,
        Red Island, Ohio, 7 August 1958

PURPOSE OF VISIT:

        To attend Second Session of Task Group,
        Inspection Engineering Handbook Conference.

PERSONNEL PRESENT

        L. M. Brown   Ord. Ammunition
        H. D. Scanlon   Ord. Tank Auto
        R. Vincent   Waterville Arsenal
        E. T. Vicuma   Aberdeen Arsenal
        T. Andrews   Red Island Arsenal
        L. P. Potter   Ord. Weapons Command
        H. S. Bowers   Lummus Arsenal

RESULTS ACCOMPLISHED AND REMARKS:

        1. Meeting opened by L. M. Brown, Chairman, at
            0900 hours.
        2. Next meeting of the group set for 19
            September 1958 at Aberdeen Arsenal.
        3. Agenda of the meeting was as follows:
            a. Introduction of Project Engineer for
                Handbook Contract.
            b. Completion of work on procedural out-
                lines for various procurement patterns.
            c. Current handling and standard phraseology
                concerning how the Agent of Inspection
                shall be designated in specifications.
        4. Minutes of the meeting are attached.
        5. A course on the preparation of Military
            Specifications will be given at Aberdeen
            Arsenal. The first class is scheduled for
            22 September 1958. Attendance by Lummus
            Arsenal representatives is recommended.

20.2.4 Specimen Letter Report

This specimen of a letter report combines the features of the typical business letter and the informal report.

You will notice that it has been written by one company to another. The mechanics of the business letter have been observed: letterhead, date, inside address, salutation, and complimentary close. These items have been put in their conventional places.

But this specimen is primarily a report. A survey has been made, certain results have been achieved, and recommendations suggested. The information could have been put in straight report form with title page, summary, and conclusions. The writer, however, showed good judgment in the form he chose. He undoubtedly felt that the letter gave a more personal tone to his report.

MOHAWK AUTOMATIC SIGNALS, INC.
Rensselaer, New York

January 6, 1958

Mr. P. O. Laughlin
Superintendent of Telegraph
New York Union Railways, Inc.
Albany, New York

> Subject: Crossing Protection at Lawrence
> Avenue, Albany, New York

Dear Mr. Laughlin:

In your letter of December 13, 1957, you stated that poor crossing conditions existed at Lawrence Avenue, Albany.

You asked this company to make a survey of the crossing conditions, with the possibility of the company providing visible and audible warning for both northward and southward train movements.

Results and Recommendation

We have completed the survey, for which specific data is appended. The results of the survey strongly indicate that serious traffic congestion exists and that a warning system should be provided.

We recommend that an annunciator system be installed at the Lawrence Avenue crossing. Such an installation would provide warning in these directions:

1. Southward on either of your main tracks for approximately 1600 feet
2. Northward on either of your main tracks for approximately 1350 feet
3. Northward on the Northern Belt Line track for approximately 1000 feet

Estimate of Costs

Our estimate to install annunciators is as follows:
Material.......................................$1545
Freight and stores........................... 210
Labor.. 735
Engineering and contingencies.............. 175

Total $2665

Installation Requirements

Your speed limit in this territory is now 20 mph for main track movements and 15 mph for movements to and from the Northern Belt Line.

If we contract to install the annunciator system, we will request that train movements over the crossing only be further reduced while installation is being made.

We will further request that during the installation the flagman be provided with a large Stop banner surfaced with reflex-reflecting sheet material.

Sincerely yours,

Murray O. Harris

Murray O. Harris
Superintendent, Signal Division

20.2.5 Specimen Letter Requesting Information

This letter is set up in a form that is widely used for business correspondence. (Many organizations do not indent for paragraphs, but simply double-space between paragraphs.)

Notice that the tone of this letter is personal and cordial. The writer has realized that he is asking a favor; therefore, he has used two basic principles for a letter of this type—he has explained why he needs the information, and he has definitely made the letter easy to answer by asking definite questions.

The language is the same as the language you would use in a report—simple, straightforward, and matter-of-fact, with no extra embellishment.

December 20, 1958

Elbert Photographic Supply Company
29 South Oak Street
Boston 20, Massachusetts

Gentlemen:

In connection with a paper I am preparing on the production of photographic slides, I should like to ask your assistance. I am a senior in chemical engineering at MIT.

So far I have not been able to get from any other source pertinent information on the coloring of negative slides. Specifically, I would like to know the steps in the process, the solutions used, and any particular techniques which have proved valuable.

I hope that I am not taking up too much of your time with my questions. I will greatly appreciate your help, and I will be very glad to send you a copy of my completed paper if you would care to look it over.

Sincerely,

Fred L. Johanssen

Fred L. Johanssen

20.2.6 Specimen Letter Giving Information

This letter is a reply to the letter of Sec. 20.2.5. Because the student made his request in readable form, the firm has been able to supply the information quickly and easily.

Note that the writer refers to the previous correspondence and that he has reacted happily to the offer made by the student. That offer helped to put the two of them on common ground. The information given is listed and numbered. The letter ends as cordially as it began.

ELBERT PHOTOGRAPHIC SUPPLY CO.
29 South Oak Street
Boston 20, Massachusetts

December 29, 1958

Mr. Fred L. Johanssen
Massachusetts Institute of Technology
Cambridge 39, Massachusetts

Dear Mr. Johanssen:

We are glad to provide you with information about the coloring of negative slides. Thank you for your offer; we should like to see a copy of your completed paper.

We find that the coloring process is done best in these three steps:

1. Apply a water-insoluble lacquer immediately around the lines or letters to be colored, to act as a dam.

2. After the lacquer has dried, paint the enclosed area with a water solution of an aniline dye.

3. After the dye has dried thoroughly, remove the lacquer with a suitable solvent.

If other colors are to be applied to the same slide, the process is repeated, a new lacquer dam being provided for each color. If the color is too dense, any excess can be removed with a damp cloth.

If you need any further information we shall be glad to supply it, or we could give you a demonstration of the process the next time we have an order for colored negative slides.

Very truly yours,
ELBERT PHOTOGRAPHIC SUPPLY CO.

Victor O. Federer

Victor O. Federer, Vice President

VOF:ba

20.2.7 Specimen Job-application Letter (Straight Letter)

It is customary to put the return address to the right of center on paper that does not have a printed letterhead.

Notice that the letter begins by orienting the reader—telling him what it is about. The writer then tells why he particularly wants to work for this company and why he feels particularly well qualified. He then identifies himself.

These preliminaries taken care of, the letter proceeds to describe the writer, beginning with the most applicable information —his practical experience and his educational background.

1426 Winter Street
Rochester 16, New York
March 27, 1958

Mr. Bernard A. Johnson
Weatherby Products Corporation
1350 Magnolia Avenue
Detroit 6, Michigan

Dear Mr. Johnson:

At the suggestion of Professor S. L. McKenzie
of the Pennsylvania Institute of Technology, I am writing
to apply for the position of junior metallurgist soon to
be open in your plant. My interest in your firm was
further stimulated by the description in a recent issue
of The Metallurgist of your work on the "Dichrom" process.
My thesis was on that subject. I should like to take
part in the further development of this process, and I
believe that my training and experience fit me particularly well for a job with Weatherby Products Corporation.

I am a senior in metallurgy at the Pennsylvania
Institute of Technology, where I shall receive a B.S.
degree early in June. Therefore I can start work any time
after June 15. I have been in the upper quarter of my
class during all four years at Tech, and I was elected to
Tau Beta Pi in my junior year.

Besides my technical training, I have had
several years of practical experience that should increase
my usefulness to a concern like Weatherby Products. Upon
graduation from high school in 1951, I went to work as a
laborer in the foundry of the Belle Engineering Corporation
in Rochester. After a year of miscellaneous manual labor
in the foundry, I was transferred to the laboratory,
where I was made a junior technician. I spent the next
two years running routine quality control tests on samples
of ferrous castings from the regular production runs of
the foundry. This work familiarized me with the preparation of metallographic samples and the operation of a
metallograph.

Working in the Belle laboratory stimulated my
interest in metallurgy, but I could see that I needed
additional formal education in order to have a successful
career in this field. Consequently I resigned from Belle
in the fall of 1954 and enrolled at Pennsylvania Tech.
During my last two years here I have worked nine hours a week
as an assistant in the Materials Testing Laboratory. This

The second page of this letter contains some of the vital statistics that are often put on a separate data sheet (see the specimen of Sec. 20.2.8). The letter closes with a request for an interview, followed by a pleasant personal touch.

The writer of this letter has used the first person throughout, although the I's are not unduly numerous. He has frankly described his own best points. Considering the purpose of the letter, do you think he sounds unpleasantly conceited? If you were an employer, wouldn't you feel that this man's writing ability would be an asset to your firm?

work has consisted primarily in supervising sophomore students in the performance of routine tensile and impact tests.

I am 25 years old, married, and the father of a 6-month-old daughter. I am a student member of the American Foundrymen's Association.

I shall be glad to come to Detroit for a personal interview whenever you want me to. If you are available on Saturdays, an appointment on that day would suit me best, since it would enable me to make the trip without missing any classes. However, if Saturday is not convenient for you, I could arrange to come on any other day, preferably a Friday.

Professor McKenzie speaks enthusiastically of you and your company, and I look forward to making your acquaintance.

Sincerely yours,

Fred A. Hatchley

20.2.8 Specimen Job-application Letter (Data Sheet and Covering Letter)

This letter-and-data-sheet is by the same man who wrote the preceding letter. The two letters open and close with essentially the same items. But this letter is considerably shorter than the other, because much of the information is tabulated in the accompanying data sheet.

Notice, however, that the writer has not depended entirely on the data sheet. He knew that a covering letter should not only set a pleasant tone, it should point out those items in the data sheet which make him stand out from other applicants.

1426 Winter Street
Rochester 16, New York
March 27, 1958

Mr. Bernard A. Johnson
Weatherby Products Corporation
1350 Magnolia Avenue
Detroit 6, Michigan

Dear Mr. Johnson:

At the suggestion of Professor S. L. McKenzie
of the Pennsylvania Institute of Technology, I am writing
to apply for the position of junior metallurgist soon
to be open at your plant.

My thesis study was on the subject of the
"Dichrom" process which your company has commercialized.
I should like to do further work on this process, and I
believe that my training and experience fit me par-
ticularly well for a job with Weatherby Products
Corporation.

I am a senior in metallurgy at the Pennsylvania
Institute of Technology, where I shall receive a B.S.
degree early in June. Other personal information, including a record of my education and work experience,
is given on the accompanying data sheet.

You will notice from the data sheet that I
have had several years of practical experience. This has
familiarized me with the preparation of metallographic
samples and the operation of a metallograph. Also, I
have had experience in working with other people in connection with my assisting in the Materials Testing
Laboratory here at Tech. My work has consisted primarily
in supervising sophomore students in the performance of
routine tensile and impact tests.

I shall be glad to come to Detroit for a
personal interview. I should prefer to come on a
Saturday, but I can make it any day you wish. Please
let me know if you want to see me.

Sincerely yours,

Fred A. Hatchley

Fred A. Hatchley

The writer of this letter has demonstrated to his prospective em-
ployer that he is capable of preparing a neat, clear form sheet.

Notice that the practical experience is given in reverse chrono-
logical order.   The latest experience is likely to be the most ad-
vanced and the most significant; an early position emphasizes it.

PERSONAL DATA SHEET

Name: Fred A. Hatchley
Address: 1426 Winter St., Rochester 16, New York
Age: 25
Citizenship: U. S.
Marital Status: Married; one child
Physical Condition: Excellent
Available: Any time after June 15, 1958

EDUCATION

Secondary School: Western High School, Rochester
Graduated 1951

College: Pennsylvania Institute of Technology
B.S. (Metallurgy), 1958 (June)

Honors: Tau Beta Pi

Offices: Vice-president, Student Chapter
American Foundrymen's Association

Senior Representative, Student Forum

Sports: Wrestling team

PRACTICAL EXPERIENCE

Organization	Position	Dates
Pennsylvania Institute of Technology Metallurgy Laboratory	Laboratory Assistant	Sept. 1956– June 1958
Belle Engineering Corp., Rochester	Junior technician in laboratory	Aug. 1952– Sept. 1954
	Laborer in foundry	July 1951– Aug. 1952
Rochester News Co.	Newsboy	1949–1951

References are often omitted from the first job-application letter and sent only if requested by the prospective employer. They should never be included in a response to a "blind ad." Always get permission before you list a man as a reference.

REFERENCES

1. Personal

> Mr. A. G. Aguard
> Professional Bldg.
> Rochester 2, N. Y.
>
> Rev. F. R. Hilton
> 126 First St.
> Rochester 13, N. Y.

2. Professional

> Prof. S. L. McKenzie
> Pennsylvania Institute of Technology
> Arcadia, Pa.
>
> Mr. J. R. Ajapadian
> Belle Engineering Corp.
> 4520 S. Oak St.
> Rochester 5, N. Y.

TYPE OF WORK DESIRED

Metallurgical laboratory work. Particularly interested in "Dichrom" process, with emphasis on development rather than manufacturing.

20.2.9 Specimen Formal Report

This report is typical of the short formal report prepared by a consulting firm for a client.

The cover would be made of cardboard, with the name of the issuing organization printed at the top. The title of the report is typed on a label in the box near the center.

The cover would be in the form of a folder, with a back leaf that is usually plain on both sides. The back leaf of the cover has been omitted from this specimen.

[Cover]

ARGYLE TESTING LABORATORY

Milray, California

EXAMINATION OF A HIGH-SPEED STEEL
CUTTER INSERT

for
Albermarle Tool Company

February 24, 1952

This title page repeats all the information on the cover, and adds the name of the writer and the addresses of the issuing and receiving organizations.

Notice that the logical blocks of information are represented by typographical blocks.

EXAMINATION OF A HIGH-SPEED STEEL
CUTTER INSERT

for

Albermarle Tool Company
Reno, Nevada

Report by

Joseph J. Connelly, Head
Metallurgy Department

Argyle Testing Laboratory
1624 North Wexter St.
Milray, California

February 24, 1952

The table of contents reproduces the heads and subheads from the text.

The list of figures is sometimes put in a separate table; often it is omitted entirely.

CONTENTS

This foreword provides general orientation and describes the purpose of the investigation. It tells who authorized the work and states that recommendations were requested.

FOREWORD

This report covers the investigation of a high-speed
steel cutter insert submitted to the Laboratory by the
Albermarle Tool Company on February 6, 1952.   The insert
was from a batch of 25 all of which were heat treated at
the same time.   All 25 inserts were found to be cracked
after the heat treatment.

Mr. H. L. Quentin, of the Albermarle Tool Company,
asked the Argyle Testing Laboratory to:

(1) Determine the cause of the crack.

(2) Ascertain whether the Dunster salt bath used
for the heat treatment could have been a primary factor in
the failure.

(3) Recommend steps to prevent repetitions of
the failure.

This summary follows the foreword. It depends on the foreword for background information. After telling very briefly what tests were performed, it gives most of its attention to the conclusions and recommendations. It presents all of the most important information contained in the report.

The recommendations can sometimes be integrated with the conclusions in a single subsection. In this report the recommendations are in a subsection separate from the conclusions because half of the conclusions do not lead to recommendations.

SUMMARY

The cracked cutter insert was subjected to a metallographic examination and an abbreviated chemical analysis. These investigations lead to the following conclusions and recommendations:

Conclusions

(1) The crack existed in the insert before the heat treatment.

(2) The crack was caused by a flaw in the steel from which the insert was made.

(3) The hardened insert had a soft case that contained austenite.

(4) The surface of the insert was contaminated with nickel from the electrode of the Dunster salt bath.

(5) The surface also contained excess carbon and nitrogen, indicating that the salts used in the bath were not neutral.

(6) Because the carbon and nitrogen, as well as the nickel, could have been factors in stabilizing the austenite and causing the soft case, the exact role of the nickel cannot be determined.

Recommendations

(1) The cracking of the cutter inserts should be taken up with the supplier of the steel from which they were made.

(2) Frequent pH determinations of the salt bath should be made, and the salts kept neutral during the heat-treating operation.

4

The discussion, in this short report, depends on the foreword for background information. After providing a little further history of the specimens, it starts to give results and conclusions mixed right in with descriptions of the work done.

DISCUSSION

The cutter inserts were heat treated in a Dunster salt bath, which uses nickel and mild-steel immersed electrodes. It was suspected that this combination had contaminated the pieces with nickel, and that the contamination had been a factor in the cracking.

The crack appeared in the middle of the back face of the insert. This is the least likely place for cracking to occur during hardening, because the back face is flat, while the front face has many sharp corners and notches.

The cracked insert was subjected to a metallographic examination and an abbreviated chemical analysis.

Metallographic Examination

The crack was very straight, extending over nearly the whole length of the part and completely by-passing two tapped holes, the only irregularities on this surface. When the insert was sectioned, it was discovered that the crack was only 3/16 inch deep.

Fig. 1 is a photomicrograph that shows considerable quantities of iron oxide in the crack. A portion of the insert was broken away with a hammer so as to expose the surfaces of the crack. Fig. 2, a photograph of the fracture, shows the oxidized condition of the crack. The fact that these surfaces were badly oxidized confirms the results of the metallographic examination.

Since there was no oxide coating on the outside surfaces of the insert as a result of the heat treatment, the very heavy deposit in the crack could not have been formed during the heat treatment. It is therefore concluded that the crack existed before the heat treatment.

A shallow, straight crack of this type with a heavy deposit of oxide is usually the result of a seam in the steel or a crack produced by improper cooling after the

Following the statements of several results and conclusions on page 5 and the top of page 6, the subsection on "Chemical Analysis" describes some of the test work done. Then follow more discussion and conclusions. The integration of results, discussion, conclusions, and description of method into one section produces a logical, clear account. Separate sections on methods and results in a report like this one would result in compartmentalization and repetition.

Notice that the description of methods, particularly the chemical analyses, are general rather than detailed. The writer assumes that his readers will believe that the Laboratory used suitable methods. He assumes that they are interested primarily in the results of the tests rather than in the details of the methods used.

rolling operation. The failures are therefore considered to be the responsibility of the steel supplier, and entirely unconnected with the heat treatment.

Hardness readings taken on the insert showed the surfaces to be soft, with a Rockwell C hardness of only 61. The core, however, yielded a reading of 65, which is of course satisfactory. A case 0.004 inch deep was found on the surface during the metallographic examination, as shown in Fig. 3. The white area at the left side is retained austenite. Since the presence of austenite would account for the soft case, a chemical analysis of the case was made to investigate the presence of carbon, nitrogen, and nickel, which act as austenite stabilizers.

Chemical Analysis

Carbon and nickel determinations were made on millings taken to a depth of 0.030 inch below the surface. Before the millings were taken, the insert was softened: it was heated to 1550 F in a lead pot, held at this temperature for 2 hours, then slowly cooled to 800 F in the pot.

The nitrogen content of the case was determined from a sliver 0.030 inch thick. The sliver was obtained by grinding away the core metal of the hardened insert on a surface grinder in order to avoid the possibility of decomposing any nitrides by a softening operation.

For comparison, carbon, nickel, and nitrogen analyses were repeated on drillings taken from the core metal. In addition, machinings taken to a depth of only 0.006 inch were analyzed for nickel. Results of the chemical analyses are given in the table below.

Partial Analysis of Cutter Insert

	% Nickel	% Carbon	% Nitrogen
Surface, 0.006 inch deep	0.34	--	--
Surface, 0.030 inch deep	0.108	0.77	0.47
Core	0.096	0.72	0.019

*Notice that the next-to-last paragraph contains a qualification—
a statement that it is impossible to tell what role the nickel played
in producing the soft case.*

*The discussion ends with several conclusions that stem from pre-
ceding observations. Several other conclusions appeared earlier.
All the important ones are restated in the summary.*

The increased content of nickel at the surface makes it evident that the insert was contaminated with nickel from the electrode of the Dunster salt bath. The increased quantities of carbon and nitrogen at the surface indicate that the salts used in the bath could not have been neutral.

Since nickel, carbon, and nitrogen all tend to stabilize austenite, it may be concluded that the use of this particular salt bath produced the soft case. Since the case contained excess carbon and nitrogen in addition to the nickel contamination, it is impossible to tell what role the nickel played in producing the soft case.

Since the crack was shown to have been present before the heat treatment, the increases in nickel, nitrogen, and carbon that took place during hardening could not have caused the crack.

The original report was hectographed. The illustrations were photographic prints pasted to the pages following the text. It would probably have been more helpful to the reader to put the photographs in suitable gaps in the text pages. But such an arrangement would have complicated production of the report, and in their present position the photographs are reasonably close to the related text.

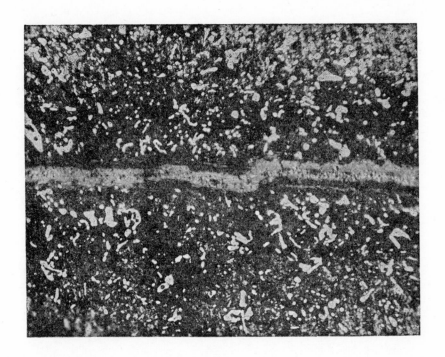

Fig. 1. Nital Etch   500x

   Photomicrograph of sample taken midway
along the crack, showing the deposit of
iron oxide in the crack.

Fig. 2. Photograph of fractured portion
of sample. The oxidized area (see arrow)
is one surface of the crack.

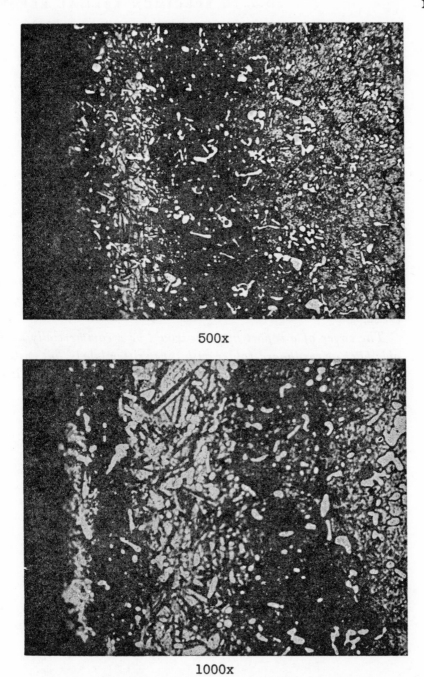

500x

1000x

Fig. 3. Nital etch. Photomicrographs taken at the edge of sample showing the presence of a case.

20.2.10 Specimen Formal Report

This report was prepared by a senior in Civil Engineering at MIT. The subject is much broader than the usual laboratory exercise.

The cover of a report like this would be a commercially available fiber or cardboard folder with typewritten labels, but without any printed legends. The back leaf of the cover has been omitted from this specimen.

SETTLEMENT OF THE
MAIN MIT BUILDINGS

APRIL 1951

Department of Civil and Sanitary Engineering
Massachusetts Institute of Technology

This title page adds to the information on the cover the name of the writer and his laboratory and the address of the organization under whose auspices the work was done.

SETTLEMENT OF THE
MAIN MIT BUILDINGS

APRIL 1951

Report by
Charles L. Miller

Soil Mechanics Laboratory
Department of Civil and Sanitary Engineering
Massachusetts Institute of Technology
Cambridge, Massachusetts

Illustrating a variation from the order of parts listed in Sec. 7.1, this report has the summary immediately after the title page, preceding the table of contents.   This arrangement permits the hurried reader to get the gist of the report immediately.   Since it precedes the foreword, this summary must supply its own orientation and background information.

The chief results of the investigation described in this report are presented in a large graph and a lengthy table.   To reduce this kind of information to a compass suitable for a summary is difficult.   Therefore this summary tends to be of the descriptive kind rather than the more useful informative kind.   Its last paragraph does, though, present a brief statement of the most significant results.

SUMMARY

In order to provide a means for determining the settlement of the main MIT buildings, brass reference markers were set in the basement columns at the time of construction. Precise elevations were established on these markers. Periodically, levels have been rerun to determine the settlement. The resultant settlement record is used to check theoretical settlement calculations.

This report presents the results of an investigation of the settlement in 1951, and describes the methods used in measuring the settlement. The settlement curve determined for 1951 is shown in Fig. 3, which also shows the complete settlement record.

Since the survey of 1938 no further settlement has occurred in Section 7   The other sections have continued to settle slightly, the maximum for the 13-year period being about 1/2 inch in Section 4.

This table of contents provides an outline of the report. It shows clearly the relationships and the relative weights of all the heads and subheads.

The list of figures could be omitted.

TABLE OF CONTENTS

This foreword provides general information about the investigation and a specific statement about the purpose of the report. It states a definite limitation on scope: the report is to present observed facts, not discuss them. Thus the report contains no conclusions or recommendations.

The foreword also lists the people connected with the investigation. This information is sometimes presented in tabular form on the title page.

FOREWORD

The Department of Civil Engineering of the Massachusetts Institute of Technology has maintained a record of
the settlement of the main MIT buildings since their construction in 1915. The last settlement readings were made
in 1938. In February 1951, the Soil Mechanics Division
decided that another set of readings should be obtained in
order to bring the record up to date.

The purpose of this report is (1) to present the results of the 1951 settlement readings and (2) to describe
the methods used in obtaining the readings. The results
are plotted in the form of a curve for easy comparison
with past settlement. It is not within the scope of this
report to discuss the reasons for the settlement.

The investigation was under the general direction of
Donald W. Taylor, Associate Professor of Soil Mechanics;
Harl P. Aldrich, Jr., Instructor in Soil Mechanics, super-
vised the work for the Soil Mechanics Division. The investigation was performed by Charles L. Miller, assisted
by Robert Woolworth, both seniors in Civil Engineering.
H. J. Shea, Associate Professor of Surveying, acted as
adviser.

This introduction provides specific and detailed background information for the investigation. It follows logically from the foreword without any substantial overlapping.

INTRODUCTION

When, in 1914, the Massachusetts Institute of Technology decided to move from their Boston location to a new
site, they chose a large tract of land on the Cambridge
bank of the Charles River. The site was ideal from the
standpoint of size and location, but the land was filled-
in swamp. Therefore, foundation conditions were very
poor. Except for fill and a sand stratum of varying
thickness, soft Boston blue clay extended to a depth of
about 120 feet below ground surface. A profile of the
building and sand stratum appears in Fig. 3 and the building plan in Fig. 4.

Substantial settlement of the massive new buildings
was expected. Boston newspapers predicted the disappear-
ance of the first floor during their readers' life time.
Although the foundation engineers did not expect such
fantastic results, they did wish to keep account of the
settlement, realizing that such a record would be valuable
to foundation engineers in the future. This information
would enable future engineers to predict settlement of
similar structures under similar conditions. Therefore
reference markers were established in most columns at the
basement level. The markers (Fig. 1) were brass plugs
inserted in the face of the columns.

During construction, precise elevations of the plugs
were established. Levels were run on the plugs in February 1915, January 1916, December 1916, July 1926, August
1933, and May 1938. The settlement record plotted from
these levels is shown in Fig. 3. Since the birth of soil
mechanics in the 1920's, this record has proved to be a
valuable tool in checking the theoretical settlement
analysis of structures.

5

Because a specially constructed tool was used in this investigation, there is some reason for the separate section on equipment. But in this early position it does tend to obscure the more important results section.

EQUIPMENT

A Berger Engineer's Tilting Dumphy Level with an 18-inch 40-power inverting telescope was used for all the instrument work.

A 7-foot wide-faced Philadelphia level rod was used for establishment of the TBM's (temporary benchmarks) and for the backsights when elevations of the settlement plugs were being measured.

A special rod was devised for the foresights on the plugs. The plugs were at such a height (5 feet 8 inches above the floor) that the line of sight of the level passed below them. The level could have been set on a box frame to obtain a line of sight high enough to read a regular rod on the plug. Instead, a rod was designed and built that would hang below the plug; see Fig. 2. This rod has the following features:

1. It places the scale at a height the instrument man can reach with a normal instrument setup.

2. It requires no rod man to hold it.

3. It can be easily aligned perpendicular to the line of sight.

4. It can be read from any angle.

5. Since the scale is mounted upside down and calibrated directly, and since the line of sight is below the point of desired elevation, no minus signs or corrections are involved: the elevation of the plug is equal to the elevation of the TBM plus the backsight plus the foresight.

6

The drawings in the original report were reproduced by Ozalid. It is not practical to put Ozalid prints on a page of text unless the text matter is typed onto the tracing of the drawing, and the whole page printed by Ozalid. This is seldom practicable. Therefore the drawings are usually printed on separate sheets. These prints may be interspersed among the text pages in convenient places following the references to them, as Figs. 1 and 2 have been here.

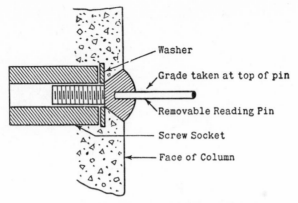

Washer

Grade taken at top of pin

Removable Reading Pin

Screw Socket

Face of Column

Fig. 1 TYPICAL SECTION THROUGH MARKER PLUG

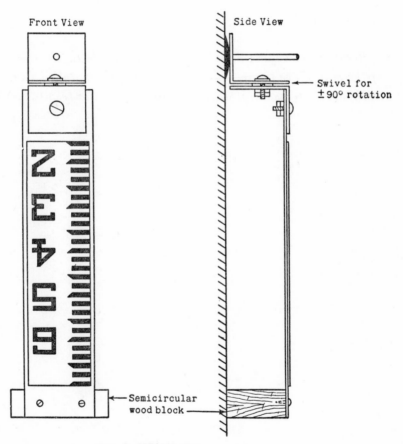

Front View

Side View

Swivel for
±90° rotation

Semicircular
wood block

Fig. 2 SPECIAL ROD

Because this report describes an investigation that was not run-of-the-mill, there is some reason for this early, detailed section on methods. But again, it does tend to obscure the results section.

GENERAL PROCEDURE

PLANNING THE WORK

The large amount of equipment, plumbing, and machinery installed in the basement in recent years has made
most of the settlement plugs extremely inaccessible.
Therefore, first, the settlement plugs were located and
classified as being:

1. Obtainable
2. Obtainable with great difficulty
3. Unobtainable.

Temporary benchmarks were next selected so as to
limit the number of instrument setups required to reach
the plugs. Wherever possible, objects in place were used
as TBM's. However, it was necessary in many places to use
heavy nails driven into the baseboard as TBM's. Fig. 4
is a plan of the main building showing the columns on
which elevations were run in 1951.

[*NOTE: The reproduction of Fig. 4 used in this book is too small for
the individual stations to be shown.*]

Finally, before the instrument work was started, the
setup positions for the level were decided on and marked.

TIE TO DATUM

In order to refer the levels to a datum, a tie was
made to the MIT Permanent Benchmark to Ledge. The elevation of this benchmark above the U. S. Coast and Geodetic
Survey (USC&GS) mean sea level datum is 9.551 feet, and
its elevation referred to the Cambridge City datum is
20.391 feet. Since the elevations obtained for the plugs
by previous runnings were referred to the Cambridge City
datum, the 1951 levels are based on an elevation of 20.391
feet. The tie from the MIT Benchmark to the TBM's was
made through a window in Building 1 (Section 1).

Near the bottom of this page is a justification for some of the methods used.

9

ESTABLISHMENT OF ELEVATIONS OF TBM'S

Differential Leveling

Elevations were established on the TBM's by differential leveling. A double check to 0.001 foot was obtained; different setups and alternate instrument men for each reading were used before the elevation of a new TBM was established.

Check and Closure

A check to the MIT Benchmark was made from Building 2 (Section 2). The error of closure was 0.003 foot. The allowable closure may be computed by:

1. Theory of Probability:
Allowable error of closure = $0.001\sqrt{n}$, where
n = number of setups

$$= 0.001\sqrt{25} = 0.005 \text{ foot.}$$

2. USC&GS Standards:
Allowable error of closure = $0.017\sqrt{m}$, where
m = distance in miles

$$= 0.017\sqrt{0.5} = 0.012 \text{ foot.}$$

Thus the closure was well within acceptable limits.

ESTABLISHING ELEVATIONS ON SETTLEMENT PLUGS

Elevations were established on the settlement plugs by differential leveling by spur lines from the TBM's. The TBM's were so located that no more than one turn was required to reach any plug. However, the many obstacles to the line of sight required exact setups to see over, under, and through motors, pipes, valves, heating ducts, and so forth.

Readers familiar with the accuracy of soil mechanics will question the need for such precision in measuring the settlement of buildings. Two reasons justify the procedure used:

1. With the exercise of such precision and care, no large accumulated error can result.

Notice the reference in the text to sample notes that have been relegated to the appendix.

2. The differential settlement from year to year, which is a matter of thousandths of a foot, is of interest to the foundation engineer, so that he can follow the rate of settlement.

FIELD NOTES

An example of the form of field notes used is shown in the Appendix on page 16. The original notes have been filed with the Office of Buildings and Power.

Since this report does not contain any discussion (see Fore-word), it has a separate section for results. The description on the opposite page points out and summarizes the most important information presented by the curve of Fig. 3 and the long table that follows.

In the original report Fig. 3 was a large folded Ozalid print. In the reproduction used in this book, Fig. 3 has been very much reduced, and it has been split so that it could go on two facing pages instead of on a folded insert. Since it is included here for purposes of illustration rather than information, the loss of detail and any misalignment between the two halves are not serious.

In the original figure, the locations of the individual marker plugs were shown within each section.

RESULTS

The elevations of the settlement plugs obtained in 1951 are given along with the original and the 1938 elevations in the table that follows. The settlement curve for 1951 was plotted as shown in Fig. 3. The curves of previous runnings are also shown.

The 1951 curve shows that the settlement is in general following its earlier pattern. However, Sections 4 and 6 have increased in rate of settlement compared to Sections 17 and 10, the previous sections of maximum settlement. The point of maximum settlement is Section 4, which has settled a total of 8.4 inches since the buildings were erected in 1915. Minimum total settlement is 1.0 inch, in Section 3. Maximum differential settlement is 7.4 inches.

As would be expected, the over-all rate of settlement has continued to decrease. Since the survey of 1938, no further settlement has occurred in Section 7. The other sections have continued to settle slightly, the maximum for the 13-year period being about 1/2 inch in Section 4.

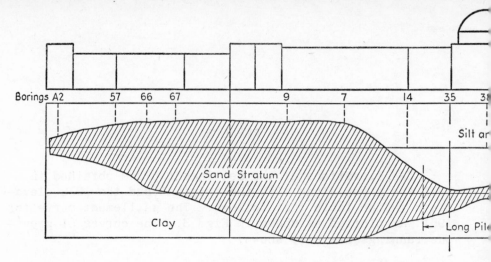

Borings A2 57 66 67   9 7 14 35 38

Silt ar

Sand Stratum

Clay

Long Pile

PROJECTION SHOWING SAND STRATU
ALONG HEAVY LINE c

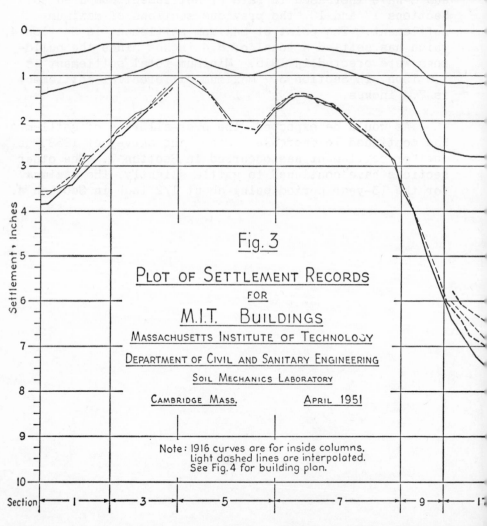

Settlement, Inches

Fig. 3

PLOT OF SETTLEMENT RECORDS

FOR

M.I.T. BUILDINGS

MASSACHUSETTS INSTITUTE OF TECHNOLOGY

DEPARTMENT OF CIVIL AND SANITARY ENGINEERING

SOIL MECHANICS LABORATORY

CAMBRIDGE MASS.   APRIL 1951

Note: 1916 curves are for inside columns.
   Light dashed lines are interpolated.
   See Fig. 4 for building plan.

Section ⊢— 1 —⊣⊢— 3 —⊣⊢— 5 —⊣⊢— 7 —⊣⊢— 9 —⊣⊢— 1?

PLOT OF SETTLEMENT ALON

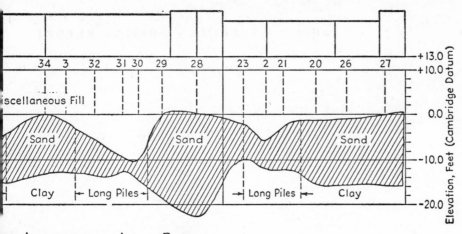

34 3 32 31 30 29   28   23 2 21 20 26 27

+13.0
+10.0

Elevation, Feet (Cambridge Datum)

scellaneous Fill

0.0

Sand   Sand   Sand

-10.0

Clay |← Long Piles →| →| Long Piles |←   Clay

-20.0

ND LOCATION OF LONG PILES

JILDING PLAN

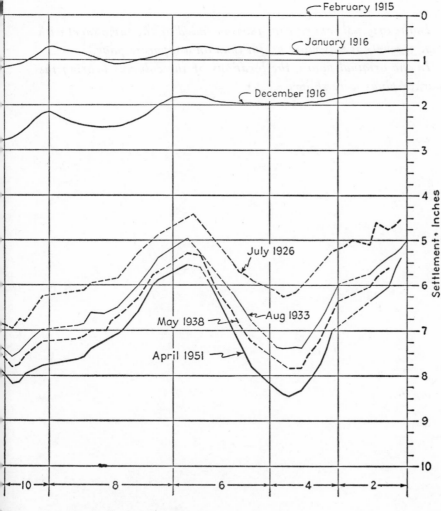

February 1915   0

January 1916   1

December 1916   2

3

4

July 1926

5

May 1938   Aug 1933   6

Settlement, Inches

April 1951   7

8

9

10

|←10→|←——8——→|←——6——→|←—4—→|←2—→|

EAVY LINE OF BUILDING PLAN

In the original report, Fig. 4 was included on the same sheet with Fig. 3, where it was more useful than on a separate page.

In the original figure, the locations of the columns bearing the marker plugs were shown.

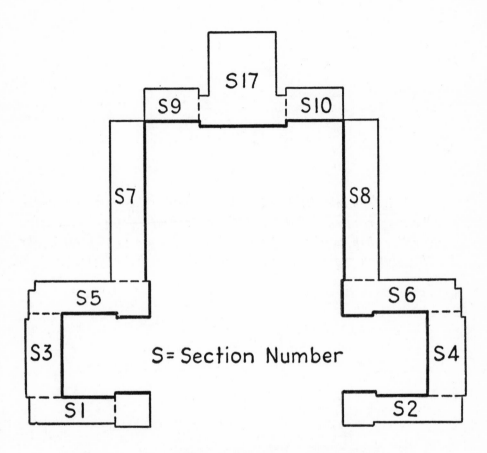

Fig. 4 Building Plan

This long table of data is put here, rather than in the appendix, because readings to thousandths of a foot—values much more precise than can be read from the curve—are of interest to the foundation engineer (see pages 9 and 10 of the report).

Elevations of Settlement Plugs
(Referred to Cambridge City Base)

Column	Feb. 1915	May 1938	April 1951
Section 1			
G-11	22.435	22.182	22.168
G'-16	22.459	22.157	22.140
G'-17	22.461	22.158	22.142
C-14	22.430	22.149	22.133
C-15	22.419	22.135	22.119
C-16	22.443	22.157	22.143
D-12	22.460	22.196	22.181
D-13	22.460	-------	22.167
E-16	22.445	22.154	22.139
E-17	22.481	22.186	22.168
F-5	22.440	22.258	22.249
G'-6	22.463	-------	22.255
Section 3			
A-2	22.439	22.250	22.244
A-3	22.455	-------	22.271
A-6	22.442	-------	22.287
A-7	22.458	22.319	22.321
A-8	22.459	-------	22.330
A-9	22.462	22.351	22.354
A-10	22.460	22.357	22.357
Section 5			
A-10	22.464	-------	22.358
A-11	22.458	22.339	22.356
A-12	22.466	22.331	22.340
B'-17	22.462	22.281	22.276
Section 7			
A-1	22.462	22.327	22.323
A-2	22.488	-------	22.362
A-3	22.469	22.351	22.350
A-5	22.451	22.337	22.334
A-6	22.472	22.356	22.352
A-7	22.453	22.322	22.332
A-9	22.442	22.308	22.306
A-10	22.433	22.291	22.287
A-11	22.434	22.277	22.272
A-12	22.457	-------	22.284
A-14	22.455	22.264	22.260
A-15	22.435	22.239	22.229

*The table in the original report contained still another half page
of figures.*

Column	Feb. 1915	May 1938	April 1951
A–17	22.456	22.235	22.230
A–18	22.477	------	22.240
Section 9			
A–1	22.441	22.202	22.188
A–3	22.466	------	22.135
A–5	22.446	------	22.040
Section 17			
B–1	22.407	21.787	21.759
D–1	22.373	21.772	21.738
F–1	22.382	21.801	21.768
F–2	22.346	21.740	21.706
G–1	22.397	21.828	21.798
J–2	22.397	21.840	21.821
Section 10			
A–2	22.433	21.784	21.753
A–3	22.437	21.794	21.764
A–4	22.437	21.811	21.778
A–7	22.433	21.835	21.792
Section 8			
G–3	22.433	------	21.953
G–4	22.427	21.947	21.925
G–5	22.429	21.928	21.908
G–6	22.427	21.908	21.884
G–9	24.118	23.567	23.533
G–11	24.469	23.889	23.871
G–13	22.430	21.848	21.817
G–14	22.432	21.841	21.806
G–15	22.432	21.835	21.799
Section 6			
A'–2	21.966	21.502	21.487
A–7	22.293	21.741	21.707
A–8	22.458	21.885	21.849
A–9	22.455	21.867	21.826
A–10	22.460	21.856	21.813
D–1	21.970	21.531	21.510

The "information on benchmarks" is proper material for the appendix, but it should have been referred to in the related text section.

The sample of field notes given here is sufficient. As stated in the report, the original notes are on file.

APPENDIX

INFORMATION ON BENCHMARKS

    1. The MIT BM to Ledge is described in USC&GS Publications and in the 1938 Report.

    2. The BM's in the buildings are described on Stone and Webster F 41034. They were used as TBM's for the 1951 levels. These elevations should not be used for future reference, since the BM's are settling with the building.

FORM OF FIELD NOTES

Record

Point	Threads B.S.	Mean	Int.	Point	Threads F.S.	Mean	Int.
	5.157		28		0.302		44
TBM B	5.129	5.129	28	7-A-12	0.258	0.258	44
	5.101				0.214		
					0.214		38
				7-A-15	0.203	0.203	38
					0.165		
	5.148		28		0.266		23
	5.120	5.120	28	7-A-14	0.243	0.243	24
	5.092				0.219		

Abstract

B.S.on	B.S.	H.I.	F.S.on	F.S.	Elev.	1915	S
TBM B	5.129	22.026	7-A-12	0.258	22.284	22.257	0.173
El.(16.897)			7-A-15	0.203	22.229	22.435	0.206
	5.120	22.017	7-A-14	0.243	22.260	22.455	0.195

REFERENCES

Plans

    Stone and Webster Engineering Corp. F 41034
SETTLEMENT PLUG LOCATIONS, MAIN GROUP (Fig. 1 and 4).

    Stone and Webster Engineering Corp. F 40235
COLUMN MARKING PLAN

Elevations of Settlement Plugs

    Stone and Webster Engineering Corp. F 60027
SETTLEMENT PLUG READINGS (Table 1).

    Mass. Institute of Technology--SETTLEMENT LEVELS by
C. A. Moore, 1938 (Table 1)

Profiles of Settlement

    Stone and Webster Engineering Corp. H 61248
SUBSIDENCE GRAPH--SECTION

    MIT Dept. of Civil Engineering, Plot of Settlement
Records, June, 1938 (Fig. 3)

Benchmark Elevations and Datums

    Stone and Webster Engineering Corp. S 61247
Bench Ties (Table 1)

    Mass. Institute of Technology SETTLEMENT LEVELS, by
C. A. Moore, 1938

20.2.11 Specimen Formal Report (Sample Pages)

The report that follows is an example of a formal research report. Only portions have been included here for inspection.

As we have already pointed out, each organization and each person writing reports must adapt the techniques of reporting to suit individual needs. It would be impossible, as well as unrealistic, to assume that any single company report could serve as a model for all reports. This report issued by Oak Ridge National Laboratory is, we think, a good example.

A standardized cover has been used. It includes title, names of authors, and file numbers. It is followed by the title page. To those items already placed on the cover have been added the names of additional personnel, the copy number, and the date issued.

The decimal system of headings has been used throughout. It first shows up in the table of contents, each item, of course, referring to a section in the text. In this report, the table of contents does not carry either the list of figures or the list of tables, which are handled on separate pages.

The abstract is a combination of the descriptive abstract and the informative abstract. It is short because a summary has been provided several pages later. Although the abstract is short, it does give specific information in the last two sentences. We looked over many reports issued by Oak Ridge. All of them used the combination of abstract and summary.

The introduction provides a method of orienting the subject matter for the reader. It discusses the problem confronting the researchers. This section is then followed by the summary, which shows in digest form how the problem was solved and what the results and conclusions were.

The conclusion to this report has been stated in simple terms; the parallel construction and numbering make it easy to read.

The reference page illustrates a variation in the arrangement of bibliography (see Sec. 16.5).

ORNL–1742
Chemistry

RADIO-FREQUENCY OSCILLATORS FOR

DETERMINATION OF ALKALI

R. W. Stelzner
M. T. Kelley

OAK RIDGE NATIONAL LABORATORY
OPERATED BY
CARBIDE AND CARBON CHEMICALS COMPANY
A DIVISION OF UNION CARBIDE AND CARBON CORPORATION

UCC

POST OFFICE BOX P
OAK RIDGE, TENNESSEE

Contract No. W-7405-eng-26

ANALYTICAL CHEMISTRY DIVISION

M. T. Kelley, Director
C. D. Susano, Associate Director

RADIO-FREQUENCY OSCILLATORS FOR DETERMINATION
OF ALKALI

R. W. Stelzner
M. T. Kelley

Edited by:
H. P. Raaen

Date Issued
JUN 9, 1955

OAK RIDGE NATIONAL LABORATORY
operated by
CARBIDE AND CARBON CHEMICALS COMPANY
A Division of Union Carbide and Carbon Chemicals Company
Post Office Box P
Oak Ridge, Tennessee

-iii-

INTERNAL DISTRIBUTION

1. C. E. Center
2. Biology Library
3. Health Physics Library
4-5. Central Research Library
6. Reactor Experimental Engineering Library
7-11. Laboratory Records Department
12. Laboratory Records, ORNL R.C.
13. C. E. Larson
14. L. B. Emlet (K-25)
15. J. P. Murray (Y-12)
16. A. M. Weinberg
17. E. H. Taylor
18. E. D. Shipley
19. F. C. VonderLage
20. M. T. Kelley
21. C. P. Keim
22. J. H. Frye, Jr.
23. W. H. Jordan
24. J. A. Swartout
25. F. L. Culler
26. S. C. Lind
27. A. H. Snell
28. A. Hollaender
29. G. H. Clewett
30. K. Z. Morgan
31. T. A. Lincoln
32. A. S. Householder
33. R. S. Livingston
34. D. S. Billington
35. C. E. Winters
36. D. W. Cardwell
37. E. M. King
38. D. D. Cowen
39. J. A. Lane
40. M. J. Skinner
41. G. E. Boyd
42. H. T. Kite (Y-12)
43. A. Krieg (Y-12)
44. D. J. Fisher
45. H. P. Raaen
46. R. W. Dodson (consultant)
47. H. Eyring (consultant)
48. J. W. Kennedy (consultant)
49. G. T. Seaborg (consultant)
50. R. H. Muller (consultant)
51. N. H. Furman (consultant)
52. ORNL Document Reference Library, Y-12 Branch

EXTERNAL DISTRIBUTION

53. R. F. Bacher, California Institute of Technology
54. Division of Research and Medicine, AEC, ORO
55-349. Given distribution as shown in TID-4500 under Chemistry category

DISTRIBUTION PAGE TO BE REMOVED IF REPORT IS GIVEN PUBLIC DISTRIBUTION

TABLE OF CONTENTS

LIST OF FIGURES

LIST OF TABLES

0.0 Abstract

The development and evaluation of an instrument for the determination of high concentrations (greater than 0.1 $\underline{M}$) of alkali in aqueous solution is described. The design of the instrument is based upon the loading of a radio-frequency oscillator. This instrument is useful in the range of 0 to 3.0 $\underline{M}$ potassium hydroxide solution.

1.0 Introduction

The adaptation of radio-frequency oscillators to the analysis of chemical systems has previously been largely in the electrolyte concentration range well below 0.1 $\underline{M}$. Harley and Wiberly, in a recent book (2), state, "Considerable work needs to be done to extend high-frequency methods to concentrated (over 0.1 $\underline{N}$) aqueous solutions." It was predicted at this laboratory that the higher Q represented in a resonant transmission-line circuit would permit greater sensitivity to concentration changes than would the Q of the conventional coil-capacitor tank circuit. The instrument described in this report was developed to take advantage of this consideration in extending the applicability of high-frequency methods to the analysis of aqueous systems of electrolyte concentration greater than 0.1 $\underline{M}$.

2.0 Summary

A radio-frequency oscillator for the determination of high concentrations (greater than 0.1 $\underline{M}$) of alkali in aqueous solution was developed and evaluated. Of the circuits considered, the most successful is a parallel transmission-line oscillator of triode type. When the cell, mounted permanently between the transmission lines, is filled with a solution of alkali, an addition is made to the power loss of the dielectric medium that surrounds the transmission lines. This increase in the power loss is reflected in terms of oscillator response by a decrease in the grid current of the oscillator. A calibration curve that relates grid current (or grid voltage) of the oscillator to concentration is used for the determination of the concentration of alkaline solutions.

The maximum drift exhibited by the parallel transmission-line oscillator is less than 0.3 mv over long periods of time when the oscillator is operated at a sensitivity of a full-scale span on a 0- to 10-mv Brown recorder; the full-scale span is equal to a 0.1 $\underline{M}$ change in the alkali concentration. This sensitivity applies to the region from 0 to about 1.0 $\underline{M}$. The sensitivity curve for the instrument indicates that the instrument operates most favorably in this lower region of concentration. It is possible to operate the instrument at concentrations above 2.5 $\underline{M}$ KOH with frequent standardization of the instrument response by means of titrations.

3.0 Principle of Operation

A radio-frequency oscillator is a device for
obtaining a periodically varying current from a steady
direct-current source. The operation of the oscillator is
dependent upon the ability of the vacuum tube to amplify a
signal that is placed upon its control grid. If a portion of the output voltage of an initially zero-biased
amplifier is fed back into the input with a phase shift of
approximately 180°, the amplifier stage can be sent into
oscillation by the application of plate voltage. The bias
of the oscillator tube is shifted rapidly from zero to a
high negative value, corresponding to Class C operation
of the tube, through the action of the grid-leak resistor
and capacitor. At the same time, the mutual trans-
conductance of the tube is reduced; this results in a
decrease in the gain of the amplifier. An equilibrium
is reached at which the circuit losses in the system are
just overcome by the amplified signal. The frequency of
these oscillations is determined by L, C, and R parameters
of the circuit, either in the form of lumped or distributed constants.

Energy at the frequency of oscillation may be
taken from the tank circuit of the oscillator by a suitable coupling scheme. Whenever radio-frequency (rf)
energy is removed from the circuit, the plate current of
the oscillator tube increases, and the grid current
decreases. The plate current increases because the
increased loss of energy from the system must be at the
expense of the direct-current source. The grid current
decreases because the voltage that is fed back to the
control grid is decreased by the lowering of the Q of the
tank circuit. Either of the two variables, plate current
or grid current, may be observed as a measure of the
energy losses of the oscillator system.

If a solution of an electrolyte is placed in the
immediate vicinity of the tank circuit of a radio-
frequency oscillator so that rf energy is absorbed from
the oscillator by the solution, changes in the plate and
grid currents of the oscillator will occur. These energy
losses, as reflected in the changes of plate and grid
currents, can be related to the concentration of the electrolyte by an empirical calibration curve in which con-

centration is plotted against either of the tube currents.
The parallel transmission-line oscillator
differs from the conventional coil-capacitor form in that
the frequency-determining parameters are distributed
constants rather than lumped constants. The distributed
constants of the transmission line permit a higher Q and a
higher impedance than is permitted for the lumped constants of the coil-capacitor form of tank circuit, at the
same frequency.

The Q of parallel transmission lines can be
calculated from the equation given by Terman,(4) that is,

$$Q = 0.0887 \ (f) \ (b) \ (J)$$

where

f = frequency, cycles per second,
b = spacing between the centers of the two
    lines, cm,
J = a factor based upon the b/a ratio of the
    transmission lines;
a = the radius of the lines.

For the transmission lines described in this report,

f = 235 Mc per second
b = 2.22 cm, and
J = 0.6;

therefore   Q = 0.0887 (235×10^6) (2.22) (0.6)
            Q = 1800 (approximately).

The value of Q calculated from this equation depends upon
negligible radiation losses and upon an air dielectric
between the transmission lines. The Q of the parallel
transmission-line oscillator will be somewhat less than
this maximum figure of 1800.

4.0 Description of Instruments

Five different designs of radio-frequency
oscillators were considered for the measurement of the
concentration of alkali in aqueous solution. Of these
designs, the most successful was a parallel transmission-
line oscillator circuit that used a type 955 acorn triode.
A modification of the basic circuit to include constant-
current control of the oscillator plate current permitted
the extension of the upper concentration limit for alkali.
Both forms of the instrument are described in this section. A dual parallel transmission-line oscillator
system that used the type 955 oscillator sections
is also described.

4.1 Parallel Transmission-Line Oscillator (PTLO)

Block and circuit diagrams of the parallel
transmission-line oscillator (PTLO) are shown in Figs.
1 and 2.

4.1.1 Oscillator

A type 955 acorn triode vacuum tube, operated
at about 235 Mc, is employed in a parallel transmission-
line oscillator circuit. The transmission lines, 8-in.
lengths of 1/8-in. copper tubing spaced 3/4 in. apart, are
soldered to the plate and to the grid pins of the tube
socket. A shorting capacitor of 800 $\mu\mu$f (zero temperature
coefficient) is moved along the parallel lines to alter
the frequency. This capacitor is soldered in place when
a frequency of 235 Mc is established. The adjustment of
frequency permits the comparison of different oscillator
sections for reproducibility of the instrumentation.
An rf filter, consisting of RFC-3 (140 μh) and its
associated 0.005-μf disk capacitors, keeps stray rf
voltages from the power supply.

The grid-leak resistor, comprised of the 25K
resistor in series with a group of measuring resistors,
develops 15 to 20 volts of negative bias when the oscillator is not loaded and when the plate voltage is +105
volts. The bias decreases to about —1 volt when the
oscillator is heavily loaded. The measuring resistors,
bypassed for rf by the 0.1-μf capacitor, are connected
to taps on a multicontact Sensitivity Switch. The

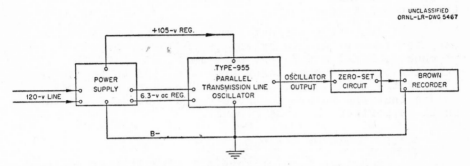

Fig. 1. Block Diagram of the Parallel Transmission-Line Oscillator.

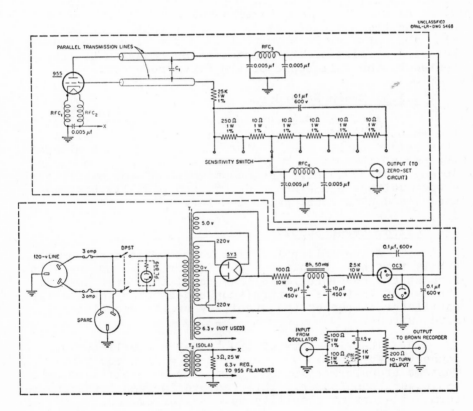

Fig. 2. Circuit Diagram of the Parallel Transmission-Line Oscillator.

oscillator output is obtained from these measuring
resistors. The switch allows control over the oscillator
output voltage that is fed into the Brown recorder via
the Zero-set Circuit.

The cathode and filaments of the 955 tube are
isolated from rf ground by the two 5/16-in. diameter
rf chokes, RFC-1 and RFC-2, each 13 turns of No. 14
enameled wire. These chokes are essential to the operation of the oscillator at this frequency because they
ensure that the inter-electrode capacitances of the tube
shall be part of the tank circuit.

4.1.2 Zero-set Circuit

A bridge type of zero-set circuit that employs
a 1.5-volt telephone battery loaded by 1.4 ma is used to
shift the zero-point of the oscillator output voltage
by $\pm$ 70 mv. This span in zero-shift can be varied by
altering the value of the 1K resistor that is in series
with the battery. This type of zero-set circuit allows a
selected portion of the concentration range to be represented by the full scale of the Brown recorder.

4.1.3 Brown Recorder

A 0- to 10-mv Brown recorder is connected to
the output of the zero-set circuit by means of a length
of shielded cable. The 10-turn Helipot zero-set allows
the pen of the recorder to be placed on the chart scale
at any desired point. The measurement of the oscillator
output voltage can also be determined manually by the
use of a conventional potentiometer.

4.1.4 Power Supply

A conventional full-wave rectification power
supply that has capacitor input filtering is employed to
furnish the power for a voltage-regulated power source.
The use of VR-tubes to furnish the d-c power for the
oscillator increases the stability of the oscillator
grid current.

The filaments of the type-955 oscillator are
connected to the 6.3-volt winding of a Sola constant-
voltage transformer instead of to the 6.3-volt winding on
the power transformer. This feature increases the short-
term grid-current stability by a factor of two.

4.1.5 Cell

The cell is a 3/4-in. diameter glass or plastic
tube that is fixed permanently between the parallel trans-

mission lines of the oscillator. A cylinder of liquid is thus placed in the electric field between the two lines. The liquid couples energy from the field, changing the plate and grid currents of the oscillator tube. This arrangement readily permits the filling and emptying of the cell; the arrangement is to be preferred to the use of sealed-in-glass standards because of the greater reproducibility in the oscillator response for a given concentration.

4.1.6 Housing

The oscillator and its cell are mounted in an 18-in. x 6-in. x 4-in. aluminum box. The power supply and the zero-set circuit are mounted within a 14-in. x 8-in. x 7-in. cabinet.

As shown in the Table of Contents, this report goes on to describe two other types of oscillators, and then contains a Discussion section. Since this report has been reproduced primarily to show the form used by one organization, these sections were omitted to save space.

6.0 Conclusions

The parallel transmission-line oscillator has the following advantages:

1. A high efficiency in the coupling of energy into the solution, i.e., in the production of power losses in the dielectric medium surrounding the lines.

2. A high degree of stability, enhanced in the lower concentration range where measuring resistors of lower values can be employed profitably.

3. A high degree of sensitivity to changes in concentration up to about 2.5 $\underline{M}$ KOH.

4. Reproducibility of an individual reading.

5. Reproducibility of instrumentation.

6. Simplicity of design.

7. No contact of the instrument, other than the cell, with corrosive or turbid solutions.

The parallel transmission-line oscillator has the following possible disadvantages:

1. Shift in mode of oscillation, resulting in a change in oscillator response.

2. Cessation of oscillations upon loading.

3. Temperature sensitivity at high instrumental sensitivity.

4. Design features based upon absolute tube characteristics.

5. Calibration altered by presence of foreign electrolytes.

If the parallel transmission-line oscillator is used without the constant-current modification (such operation is entirely feasible in the concentration range up to about 1.0 $\underline{M}$), it has the advantages of simplicity, a high sensitivity to changes in alkali concentration, a high order of stability, reproducibility of instrumentation, and reproducibility of an individual reading. The reproducibility of the instrumentation was demonstrated by the testing of three different oscillator sections (all operated at about 235 Mc) in the instrument. These sections gave almost identical responses.

If the parallel transmission-line oscillator is used with the constant-current modification, the concentration range can be extended upward to concentrations that approach 3.0 $\underline{M}$, with all the above listed advantages except that of simplicity.

An oscillator can shift from one mode of oscillation to another under the influence of circuit transients. If the two modes have similar circuit losses, the oscillator prefers that mode in which the losses are least. This shift in mode of oscillation could result in a discontinuity in the calibration curve if widely different grid currents were associated with the two modes of oscillation. The parallel transmission-line oscillators exhibited relative freedom from these shifts in oscillator mode.

Although the parallel transmission-line oscillator was loaded in taking power from the tank circuit so that the grid voltage of the type 955 tube increased from -20 to -1 volt, the oscillator was never observed to cease oscillating. The presence of a negative grid voltage was taken as an indication of oscillation.

When the instrument is operated at its highest sensitivity, a dependence of oscillator response on temperature appears, probably arising from a change in the conductance of the solution. This temperature dependence could be removed by thermostatting the cell.

It would be desirable to design an oscillator that would be independent of tube characteristics, but this does not appear possible with a self-excited oscillator. The parallel transmission-line oscillator tolerates a considerable variation in the values of tube parameters. Different type 955 tubes produce almost identical slopes for the calibration curves. The Zero-set control can be used to correct for any variation in tube characteristics.

The response of the parallel transmission-line oscillator depends upon the total conductance of the solution in the cell. Any foreign electrolyte present in the cell solution will affect the oscillator response,

thus causing an inaccuracy in the determination of the
concentration of the alkaline species. This criticism is
applicable to any rf instrument that depends upon the
loading of an oscillator, and it is not unique with the
parallel transmission-line model.

Use of the parallel transmission-line oscillator
is not restricted to the analysis of alkaline solutions,
although such solutions were employed in most of the
above work. As an example of the sensitivity of this rf
instrument to measure the concentration of a different
electrolyte, two solutions of NaCl of concentrations of
36 g per 100 ml and 18 g per 100 ml gave readings of 13.0
and 19.3 mv, respectively, a span of 6.3 mv in the
oscillator response. When strong solutions of aqueous
sulfuric acid are placed in the cell, the parallel
transmission-line oscillator is sensitive to changes in
the sulfuric acid concentration. Figure 17 gives a
calibration curve for sulfuric acid in the very high
concentration region.

-38-

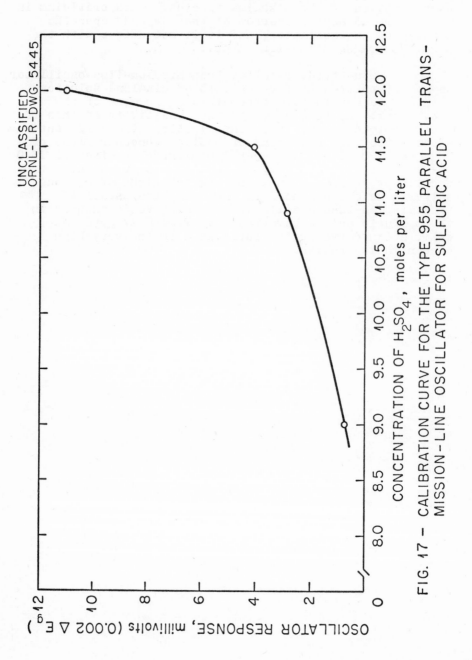

FIG. 17 – CALIBRATION CURVE FOR THE TYPE 955 PARALLEL TRANS-
MISSION-LINE OSCILLATOR FOR SULFURIC ACID

7.0 References

1. Blaedel, W. J. and Malmstadt, H. V., "High-Frequency Titrations," Anal. Chem., 22, 1413 (1950).

2. Harley, J. H. and Wiberley, S. E., Instrumental Analysis, p. 300, John Wiley, New York, 1954.

3. Terman, F. E., Radio Engineering, 2nd ed., pp. 362-363, McGraw-Hill Book Company, Inc., New York, 1937.

4. Terman, F. E., Radio Engineer's Handbook, p. 192, McGraw-Hill Book Company, Inc., New York, 1943.

20.2.12 Specimen Letter of Transmittal

The specimen reproduced here illustrates some of the principles and functions of the letter of transmittal.

The survey referred to was obviously made on assignment. Under this circumstance, the writer undoubtedly felt that a letter of transmittal would be appropriate. He was able, therefore, to direct the report to a specific person within the organization.

In addition to transmitting the report, the letter provides the reader with a general orientation into the subject matter. It goes on to enumerate the objectives of the survey.

In the last paragraph, the letter makes a pertinent comment about the limits imposed on the survey. It closes by making a definite recommendation about future action.

MARTIN ASSOCIATES, INC.

Management Consultants
Hollywood, California

August 25, 1958

The Federal Reserve Bank of Santa Fe
20 Diamond Street
Santa Fe, New Mexico

Attention: Mr. George Sissell, First Vice President

Gentlemen: C-58496

We are submitting a report on a survey covering fields of
industrial opportunity in the Southwest.

The survey was based on a review of the material and
human resources of the region, and on technological
advance. The objective was to discover new markets for
products now made by Southwestern companies, methods for
introducing newly developed products, and opportunities
for establishing new industries suitable for the region.
The emphasis has been placed principally on growth
industries.

Because many of the staff members of Martin Associates,
Inc., contributed technical analyses of products, the
result has been a symposium covering a broad range of
industrial processes and situations.

The purpose of the survey was only to identify manufacturing opportunities justifying further investigation.
Interested organizations will, of course, require that
those investigations be made before they commit themselves financially.

Respectfully submitted,

John J. Martin

JJM:arw

368 20.2.13 SPECIMEN FORMAL INSTRUCTIONS

20.2.13 Specimen Formal Instructions

This sample of formal instructions is from a manual dealing with a digitally controlled tube tester manufactured by International Business Machines. The manual as a whole contains sections describing the problem of designing the tube tester, the solution to the problem, the operation of the device, and tests for characteristics of tubes.

We have reproduced only the section on operation to show to what extent company practice follows the principles we have suggested for formal instructions (see Sec. 11.2).

The title is descriptive and brief. The specific instructions for operating the tube tester have been stated in the imperative mood. Under 5 occurs a note or explanation; this has been written in the indicative mood.

The instructions have been numbered, with each confined to a separate paragraph. Capitalization plus quotation marks gives more emphasis than necessary to the identification of parts (see Secs. 16.3 and 16.4.3).

THE DIGITALLY CONTROLLED
TUBE TESTER

OPERATION

1. Turn on main switch and wait for green light.

2. Insert tubes from left to right.

3. Move switches:
   a. The "CALIBRATE" switch to "RUN" position
   b. The "SOCKET" switch to "MANUAL" position
   c. The "TEST" switch to "AUTOMATIC" position

4. Push "START" button.

5. When machine starts, set "SOCKET" switch to "AUTOMATIC" position.

   A tube defect will stop the machine. A lamp on the side of the socket will show which tube is under test. A red light on the meter panel will indicate the nature of the fault.

6. To start the machine after a defect has been located, depress the "START" button and wait for the machine to clear the bad tube before pulling it out.

7. If at any time manual operation is desired from socket to socket or test to test, turn the respective socket or test switch to "MANUAL" position and depress the adjacent button.

8. To stop the machine when in automatic operation, depress the "STOP" button.

Tubes cannot be inserted into the bank of sockets not being used.

20.3 Bibliography

Dictionaries

The American College Dictionary. New York: Random House, 1958.

Tweney, C. F., and Hughes, L. E. C. *Chambers's Technical Dictionary* (third edition). New York: The Macmillan Co., 1958.

Webster's New Collegiate Dictionary. Springfield: G. and C. Merriam Co., 1956.

Webster's Dictionary of Synonyms. Springfield: G. and C. Merriam Co., 1951.

Handbooks and Textbooks

Evans, Bergen, and Evans, Cornelia. *Contemporary American Usage* (*A Dictionary of*). New York: Random House, 1957.

Fowler, H. W. *Modern English Usage* (*A Dictionary of*). New York: Oxford University Press, 1926.

————, and Fowler, F. G. *The King's English.* Oxford: Oxford University Press, 1931.

Gaum, Carl G., Graves, Harold F., and Hoffman, Lyne S. S. *Report Writing* (third edition). Englewood Cliffs, N. J.: Prentice-Hall, Inc., 1950.

Geist, Robert J., and Summers, Richard. *Current English Composition.* New York: Rinehart and Co., 1951.

Gunning, Robert. *The Technique of Clear Writing.* New York: McGraw-Hill Book Co., 1952.

Kapp, Reginald O. *The Presentation of Technical Information.* New York: The Macmillan Company, 1957.

Mills, Gordon H., and Walter, John A. *Technical Writing.* New York: Rinehart and Co., 1954.

Perrin, Porter G. *Writer's Guide and Index to English* (revised edition). Chicago: Scott, Foresman and Co., 1950.

Sherman, Theodore A. *Modern Technical Writing.* Englewood Cliffs, N. J.: Prentice-Hall, Inc., 1955.

Shurter, R. L. *Written Communication in Business.* New York: McGraw-Hill Book Co., 1957.

Souther, James W. *Technical Report Writing.* New York: John Wiley & Sons, 1957.

Thomas, J. D. *Composition for Technical Students* (revised edition). New York: Charles Scribner's Sons, 1949.

Turabian, Kate L. *A Manual for Writers of Term Papers, Theses, and Dissertations* (revised edition). Chicago: University of Chicago Press, 1955.

University of Chicago Press. *A Manual of Style.* Chicago, 1949.

Technical Society Publications

American Chemical Society. *Hints to Authors* (Bulletin 8). Washington, 1949.

American Institute of Electrical Engineers. *Information for Authors.* New York, 1948.

American Standards Association. *Abbreviations for Scientific and Engineering Terms* (Z10.1–1941). New York, 1941.

———— *Abbreviations for Use on Drawings* (32.13–1950). New York, 1950.

———— *Style Manual for American Standards* (PM 117). New York, 1949.

Engineers' Council for Professional Development. *Speaking Can Be Easy . . . for Engineers too.* New York, 1950.

Miscellaneous

Masterson, James R., and Phillips, Wendell Brooks. *Federal Prose.* Chapel Hill: The University of North Carolina Press, 1948.

Quiller-Couch, Sir Arthur Thomas. "On Jargon," from *On the Art of Writing*. New York: G. P. Putnam's Sons, 1950.

Strunk, William, Jr., and White, E.B. *The Elements of Style*. New York: The Macmillan Co., 1959.

Wall, Florence E. "The Essentials of a Good Report." *Journal of Chemical Education*, March 1947.

———— "Requirements and Responsibilities of a Technical Editor." *Journal of Chemical Education*, October 1953.

INDEX

INDEX